Dec. 29, 1978

Dear Tracey,

This book was written by your
great-grandfather. I know he'd
like you to have a copy.

Love,
Dad

The Origin

and

History of the Earth

by

ROBERT TUNSTALL WALKER,
Formerly Chief Geologist, United States Smelting, Refining and
Mining Company, Salt Lake City, Utah.

and

WOODVILLE JOSEPH WALKER,
Formerly Geologist, Resurrection Mining Company, Leadville, Colorado.

THE WALKER CORPORATION
Box 1068
Colorado Springs, Colorado
1954.

Price: $5.00 postpaid in the United States.
5.25 postpaid in Canada and Mexico.
5.50 postpaid in other countries.

PRINTED BY

BRADFORD-ROBINSON PRINTING COMPANY

1824 STOUT ST., DENVER, COLORADO

To

MARY ELIZABETH WALKER,
wife and mother.

Preface

Progress in human knowledge takes place chiefly by trial and error. When a sufficient number of observations have accumulated, all seemingly pointed in one general direction, the conclusions they indicate are summarized in the form of an Hypothesis. If further information tends to support this Hypothesis, it may be elevated to the higher status of a Theory, and if eventually no exceptions to it are discovered, it may by general consent achieve unopposed recognition as a Fact or Law. But if many irregularities and inconsistencies develop in the original Hypothesis, it may be necessary to modify it somewhat, or even to drop it entirely and substitute another quite different. Such a procedure is rarely accomplished without friction between the adherents of the old Hypothesis and the proponents of the new one. The churchmen, who, on the authority of the Bible, contended that the Earth was flat, bitterly opposed and often persecuted as a heresy, the later belief that the Earth was spherical in shape,—now accepted as a Fact. The Hypothesis that the Earth was the center of the Solar System, supported by the authority of the eminent Egyptian astronomer, Ptolemy, persisted for several centuries after the Polish astronomer Copernicus had shown that, instead, the Sun was its center,—now also accepted as a Fact.

An Hypothesis, which has been accepted by most geologists and astronomers for the past hundred years, is that the Earth is shrinking in volume. During this period, however, many prominent geologists, impressed by its inconsistencies, have questioned its validity, but without proposing a substitute Hypothesis, that would be more acceptable. The authors of this book, economic geologists, with a joint span of experience covering over fifty years of surface and underground observations, finding themselves confronted by more and more geological evidence, which could not possibly be reconciled with that Hypothesis, were slowly and reluctantly forced to the opposite conclusion that the Earth was increasing in volume, and that the cause of this phenomenon must be some expanding mass at the center of the Earth. This idea once adopted, the phenomena of vulcanism and orogeny,—heretofore inadequately explained,—all fell into place like the parts of a jigsaw puzzle. The next task was to investigate the nature of this supposed central expanding mass. The trail led first into nuclear physics, then into astronomy, and finally into cosmogony; and, by utilizing accepted astronomical data it was possible to reach a conclusion as to the probable nature and origin of this central mass. The most logical method of setting forth this conclusion might have been to commence with the generally accepted facts of geology, relating to the nature of the Earth, and to have progressed outwardly from that starting point. But the first duty of an author to his readers is to make himself clear and convincing, and for this reason the opposite but more systematic plan of commencing with a description of the nature of the Universe, and thence working down progressively to the origin and history of the Earth, has been adopted. The general conclusions set forth in this book as to the origin of the Earth and of the Universe are contrary to those held by most scientists at the present time, and hence it is to be understood that they are proposed only as an Hypothesis, whose ultimate acceptance or rejection will depend upon further investigation by scientists of the evidence and assumptions on which it is based. The authors, meanwhile, accept entire responsibility for proposing it herewith.

Contents

Illustrations

CHAPTER ONE

Fundamentals

Although many thousand different forms of chemical compounds exist in nature and many thousand others have been made artificially, they are all composed of what are called the chemical elements, usually in combinations of two or more such elements in various proportions and arrangements. An element is a substance, which cannot be broken down by chemical means into simpler substances. Of the ninety-eight elements so far discovered, as listed on the following table, eleven (argon, chlorine, fluorine, helium, hydrogen, krypton, neon, nitrogen, oxygen, radon and xenon) are gases, two (bromine and mercury) are liquids, and the others are solids, at normal temperature and pressure. Eighty-eight of the elements have been found in nature; the other ten (technetium, promethium, astatine, francium, neptunium, plutonium, americium, curium, berkelium and californium) have been formed artificially. Sixty-six of the elements have been identified in the Sun by spectroscopic analysis, and many of them have also been found in the same way in some of the stars. But no element, not already recognized on the Earth, has been found in the Sun and stars, although helium was discovered in the Sun before it was found on the Earth. As later discussed, however, it is probable that other and heavier elements than those now known exist deep within the bodies of the Earth, the Sun and the stars.

The elements were once thought to be indivisible, but it is now known that they are all composed of three fundamental particles: a relatively light particle, called the electron, which carries a negative electrical charge equal to 4.80×10^{-10} absolute electrostatic unit; a relatively heavy particle called the proton, which carries a positive electrical charge, exactly equal in magnitude to the negative electrical charge of the electron; and another relatively heavy particle called the neutron, which carries no electrical charge. The neutron is a composite structure, as shown by the fact that, when in the free state, it disintegrates spontaneously and rapidly into an electron,

1

TABLE I.

TABLE OF ELEMENTS.

Atomic Number	Name	Atomic Weight	Atomic Number	Name	Atomic Weight
1.	Hydrogen (H)	1.008	41.	Niobium	
2.	Helium (He)	4.003		(Columbium) (Nb)	92.91
3.	Lithium (Li)	6.940	42.	Molybdenum (Mo)	95.95
4.	Beryllium		43.	Technetium (Tc)	99.0 *
	(Glucinum) (Be)	9.013	44.	Ruthenium (Ru)	101.7
5.	Boron (B)	10.82	45.	Rhodium (Rh)	102.91
6.	Carbon (C)	12.01	46.	Palladium (Pd)	106.7
7.	Nitrogen (N)	14.008	47.	Silver (Ag)	107.88
8.	Oxygen (O)	16.000	48.	Cadmium (Cd)	112.41
9.	Fluorine (F)	19.00	49.	Indium (In)	114.76
10.	Neon (Ne)	20.183	50.	Tin (Sn)	118.70
11.	Sodium (Na)	22.997	51.	Antimony (Sb)	121.76
12.	Magnesium (Mg)	24.32	52.	Tellurium (Te)	127.61
13.	Aluminum (Al)	26.97	53.	Iodine (I)	126.92
14.	Silicon (Si)	28.06	54.	Xenon (X)	131.3
15.	Phosphorus (P)	30.98	55.	Cesium	
16.	Sulphur (S)	32.066		(Caesium) (Cs)	132.91
17.	Chlorine (Cl)	35.457	56.	Barium (Ba)	137.36
18.	Argon (A)	39.944	57.	Lanthanum (La)	138.92
19.	Potassium (K)	39.096	58.	Cerium (Ce)	140.13
20.	Calcium (Ca)	40.08	59.	Praseodymium (Pr)	140.92
21.	Scandium (Sc)	45.10	60.	Neodymium (Nd)	144.27
22.	Titanium (Ti)	47.90	61.	Promethium (Pm)	147.0 *
23.	Vanadium (V)	50.95	62.	Samarium (Sm)	150.43
24.	Chromium (Cr)	52.01	63.	Europium (Eu)	152.0
25.	Manganese (Mn)	54.93	64.	Gadolinium (Gd)	156.9
26.	Iron (Fe)	55.85	65.	Terbium (Tb)	159.2
27.	Cobalt (Co)	58.94	66.	Dysprosium (Dy)	162.46
28.	Nickel (Ni)	58.69	67.	Holmium (Ho)	164.94
29.	Copper (Cu)	63.54	68.	Erbium (Er)	167.2
30.	Zinc (Zn)	65.38	69.	Thulium (Tm)	169.4
31.	Gallium (Ga)	69.72	70.	Ytterbium (Yb)	173.04
32.	Germanium (Ge)	72.60	71.	Lutecium (Lu)	174.99
33.	Arsenic (As)	74.91	72.	Hafnium	
34.	Selenium (Se)	78.96		(Celtium) (Hf)	178.6
35.	Bromine (Br)	79.916	73.	Tantalum (Ta)	180.88
36.	Krypton (Kr)	83.7	74.	Wolfram	
37.	Rubidium (Rb)	85.48		(Tungsten) (W)	183.92
38.	Strontium (Sr)	87.63	75.	Rhenium (Re)	186.31
39.	Yttrium (Y)	88.92	76.	Osmium (Os)	190.2
40.	Zirconium (Zr)	91.22	77.	Iridium (Ir)	193.1

* Mass number of longest lived isotope.

TABLE I.—Continued

Atomic Number	Name	Atomic Weight	Atomic Number	Name	Atomic Weight
78.	Platinum (Pt)	195.23	89.	Actinium (Ac)	227.05
79.	Gold (Au)	197.2	90.	Thorium (Th)	232.12
80.	Mercury (Hg)	200.61	91.	Protactinium (Pa)	231.0
81.	Thallium (Tl)	204.39	92.	Uranium (U)	238.07
82.	Lead (Pb)	207.21	93.	Neptunium (Np)	237.0 *
83.	Bismuth (Bi)	209.0	94.	Plutonium (Pu)	239.0 *
84.	Polonium (Po)	210.0	95.	Americium (Am)	241.0 *
85.	Astatine (At)	210.0 *	96.	Curium (Cm)	242.0 *
86.	Radon (Rn)	222.0	97.	Berkelium (Bk)	243.0 *
87.	Francium (Fr)	223.0 *	98.	Californium (Cf)	246.0 *
88.	Radium (Ra)	226.05			

* Mass number of longest lived isotope.

FOOTNOTE: In scientific literature, it is often convenient to express numbers —and particularly very large and very small numbers—as factors of appropriate powers of ten. Thus, 5,000,000,000 may be written 5×10^9, indicating that nine zeros follow the digit; while 0.000,000,005 may be written 5×10^{-9}, indicating that the digit occupies the ninth place beyond the decimal point. More complex numbers may be similarly expressed, as follows:

$$5,240,000,000 \text{ may be written } 5.24 \times 10^9$$
$$524 \text{ may be written } 5.24 \times 10^2$$
$$0.0524 \text{ may be written } 5.24 \times 10^{-2}$$
$$0.000,000,524 \text{ may be written } 5.24 \times 10^{-7}$$

This method will be frequently employed in this book. Most scientific measurements are expressed in terms of the metric system, and the following are those most commonly used in this book.

Measurements of length.
Small.   Centimeter (cm) : 0.3937 inch.
Large.   Kilometer (km) (10^5 centimeters) : 0.621372 mile.

Measurements of area.
Small.   Square centimeter (cm^2) : 0.155 square inch.
Large.   Square kilometer (km^2) (10^{10} cm^2) : 0.3861006 square mile.

Measurements of volume.
Small.   Cubic centimeter (cm^3) : 0.0610234 cubic inch.
Large.   Cubic kilometer (km^3) (10^{15} cm^3) : 0.2399121 cubic mile.

Measurements of mass or weight.
Small.   Gram (g) : 0.03527396 ounces avoirdupois.
Large.   Kilogram (kg) (10^3 g) : 2.2046223 pounds avoirdupois.

The short ton of 2,000 pounds avoirdupois is the one used in this book.

a proton, and aneutrino,—the latter being a form of radiation, as later described. A proton weighs about 1837 times as much as an electron, while a neutron is a trifle heavier than a proton. All are nearly the same size,—the electron, despite its much smaller mass, being somewhat the largest. All are excessively minute, being less than a millionth of a millionth of an inch in diameter, and weighing less than a millionth of a millionth of a millionth of a millionth of an ounce, as shown by the following table:

Particle.	Diameter.	Mass.
Electron.	5×10^{-13} centimeter.	9.10721×10^{-28} gram.
Proton.	3×10^{-13} centimeter.	1.67321×10^{-24} gram.
Neutron.	3×10^{-13} centimeter.	1.6754×10^{-24} gram.

The unit or smallest particle of an element is called an atom. Each atom consists of a central part, called the nucleus, around which one or more electrons circle like planets around the Sun, and hence are called orbital, planetary, or circumnuclear electrons. The nucleus consists of one or more protons and one or more neutrons, except in the case of normal hydrogen, whose nucleus is a single proton. The protons and neutrons of the nucleus are tightly held together by a mutual attraction, which leads to a very large binding energy.

The superficial resemblance of the structure of an atom to the Solar System, wherein the nucleus plays the part of the Sun and the electrons the planets, is heightened by the fact that each electron, in addition to revolving around a nucleus, also spins or rotates on its axis, which is perpendicular to the plane of its orbit, while the nucleus also rotates on its own axis. The speed of revolution of the electron and the speed of rotation of the electron and the nucleus, are enormous. Thus, in the case of the normal hydrogen atom, the single electron, which travels in an orbit with a diameter of 1.058×10^{-8} centimeter around the nucleus, moves with a speed of 2.19×10^{8} centimeters (over 1200 miles) per second, so that it is not surprising that it makes 6.59×10^{15} revolutions per second. Similarly, this electron rotates on its axis 3.68×10^{26} times per second, while the nucleus rotates on its axis 5.55×10^{23} times per second.

This superficial resemblance of the structure of an atom to that of the Solar System, however, does not extend to the distribution and arrangement of the orbits, for while the orbits of the planets lie nearly in one plane and at random although fixed distances from the Sun, the orbits of the electrons around a nucleus occur in various

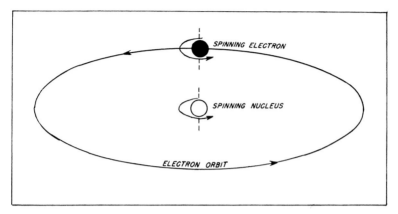

FIGURE 1 - 1

Illustrating diagrammatically the atomic structure of the hydrogen atom. Not drawn to scale,—the sizes of the nucleus and electron being greatly exaggerated. (*"Classical and Modern Physics"*, by Harvey E. White, p. 523. Copyright, 1940, D. Van Nostrand Company, Inc., New York, N. Y.)

attitudes but in somewhat definite positions with respect to it, spaced with reference to a series of imaginary concentric spheres called "shells." The diameters of the successive shells vary according to the squares on the numbers of such shells outwardly from the nucleus. Thus the diameter of the second shell is four times (2^2) that of the first shell; the diameter of the third shell is nine times (3^2) that of the first shell; and so on. Each shell, after the first, is divided into two or more sub-shells. The shells and sub-shells do not mark the actual positions of orbits, but only the vicinity where they are most likely to occur; and only a certain number of orbits may occur in the vicinity of each shell and sub-shell. The orbits tend to be elliptical in the inner sub-shells of a shell and circular in the outer sub-shells, but as a matter of fact the paths followed by the electrons may be very complicated, so that it is not possible to fix them definitely and with precision, but only within a certain degree of probability.

The number of electron orbits, which each shell or sub-shell can contain, is limited to a certain maximum, which is the same for all atoms. The electron shell nearest the nucleus is filled first; then the sub-shell next outwardly; and this procedure customarily continues, with each sub-shell being completed before the filling of the next one outwardly is commenced. This rule, however, does not hold for the more complex atoms, some of whose electrons may occupy orbits in the outer shells, before the inner shells are completely filled. This is illustrated in the case of uranium, which has 92 orbital electrons.

Shell	Sub-shell	Number of electrons actually occupying each shell and sub-shell	Maximum capacity of each shell for electrons
1st (K)	1s	2	2
2nd (L)	2s	2	8
	2p	6	
3rd (M)	3s	2	18
	3p	6	
	3d	10	
4th (N)	4s	2	32
	4p	6	
	4d	10	
	4f	14	
5th (O)	5s	2	50
	5p	6	
	5d	10	
	5f	3	
6th (P)	6s	2	72
	6p	6	
	6d	1	
7th (Q)	7s	2	98

This behavior is due to the fact that, since the electron orbits in the inner sub-shells of a given shell are eccentric ellipses while those in the outer sub-shells are circular, the inner electron orbits of an outer sub-shell may approach the nucleus more closely, in sections of their paths, than the outer electron orbits of an inner sub-shell, and hence be more attractive to an electron.

The chemical properties of each atom are determined wholly by the orbital electrons it contains, and principally by the outer electrons. In a normal atom the number of protons in the nucleus always equals the number of orbital electrons. The normal hydrogen atom contains only one proton, with no neutron, but with this exception all atoms contain both protons and neutrons in their nuclei. The ratio of protons to neutrons in the nucleus of any atom, however, is not fixed, but may vary within certain limits, so that varieties of a chemical element may exist, all containing the same number of protons, but different numbers of neutrons, in the nucleus. Such varieties, which are chemically identical and cannot be separated by chemical means, are called isotopes.

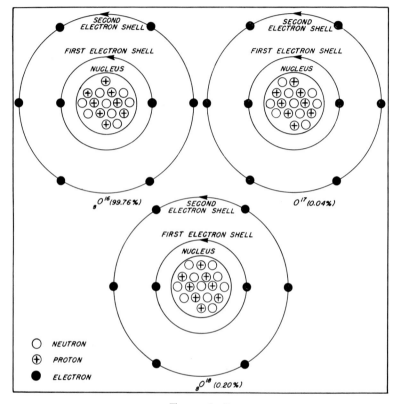

FIGURE 1 - 2

Illustrating diagrammatically the atomic structures of the three natural isotopes of oxygen. Not drawn to scale,—the sizes of the nuclei, neutrons, protons and electrons being greatly exaggerated.

Those isotopes, which exist in nature, are called natural isotopes; while those isotopes, which do not exist in nature, but can be made artificially, are called artificial isotopes. The number of protons in the nucleus of an isotope is called the atomic number, while the total number of protons and neutrons in such nucleus is called the mass number. The number of neutrons in such a nucleus, therefore, is the difference between the mass number and the atomic number. For each isotope, the atomic number is indicated by a subscript before the symbol of the element and the mass number by a superscript after this symbol. Thus the sole natural isotope of beryllium (Be),

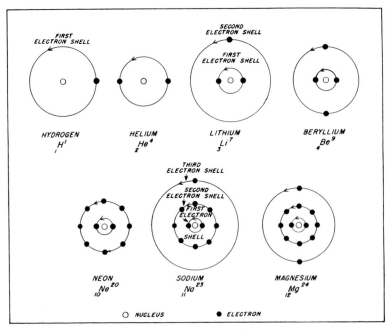

FIGURE 1 - 3

Illustrating diagrammatically the atomic structures and comparative sizes of the principal natural isotopes of some of the simpler atoms. Not drawn to scale,—the sizes of the nuclei and electrons being greatly exaggerated. ("*Classical And Modern Physics*," by Harvey E. White, p. 523. Copyright, D. Van Nostrand Company, Inc., New York, N. Y.)

whose nucleus contains four protons and five neutrons, is symbolized by $_4Be^9$. The atomic weight of an isotope is the ratio of its mass, consisting of the combined weight of the protons, neutrons and electrons composing it, to one sixteenth the mass of oxygen, which is arbitrarily taken to be 16.00,—the mass number of its principal isotope. Since most of the weight of an isotope resides in the protons and neutrons composing its nucleus, the atomic weight is always close to the mass number.

It is theoretically possible for a very large number of isotopes to occur, but only those actually exist in nature or can be made artificially, in which the number of protons does not differ very largely from the number of neutrons in the nucleus. Twenty-three of the ninety-eight known elements have only one natural isotope each, but all the others occur in nature as mixtures of two or more isotopes, and consequently their atomic weights are the averages of the atomic weights of their constituent isotopes. It is interesting to note that elements with an even atomic number, occurring in nature, may have up to ten stable isotopes, while those with an odd atomic number never have more than two stable isotopes. In addition to the natural stable isotopes, of which 280 have now been recognized, some 40 or so naturally occurring unstable isotopes have been discovered, while close to 700 unstable isotopes have been prepared artificially. All isotopes with an atomic number above 83 are unstable, while all natural isotopes with an atomic number below 80 are stable, save for a few unimportant exceptions, of which the potassium isotope $_{19}K^{40}$ is the most abundant. Except for hydrogen and one isotope of helium, which contains two protons and only one neutron, the number of neutrons is never less than the number of protons in any stable nucleus. In fourteen natural isotopes the number of neutrons exactly equals the number of protons in their nuclei, but in all other stable isotopes the number of neutrons in the nucleus exceeds the number of protons, and the higher the atomic number the greater the excess of neutrons over protons, both numerically and relatively, up to a maximum of about 54%. There is, however, a limit to the number of neutrons in excess of protons, that a nucleus may contain, without becoming unstable, and this explains the fact that there are no stable isotopes with a mass number above 209. Iron, with an atomic number 26, provides a good example of an element, which in nature is a mixture of isotopes:

	Natural stable isotopes.	Natural abundance.	Artificially produced unstable isotopes.
	$_{26}Fe^{54}$	5.84%	$_{26}Fe^{52}$
	$_{26}Fe^{56}$	91.68%	$_{26}Fe^{53}$
	$_{26}Fe^{57}$	2.17%	$_{26}Fe^{55}$
	$_{26}Fe^{58}$	0.3 %	$_{26}Fe^{59}$
Average:	$_{26}Fe^{55.73}$	100.0 %	
Atomic weight:	55.85		

The relative proportions of natural isotopes in atoms are usually about the same in substances obtained from widely different sources, although slight differences have been observed.

Isotopes of different chemical elements, which have the same mass number or total number of protons and neutrons in the nucleus, but different amounts of each, are called isobars. Thus, sulphur has an isotope containing 16 protons and 20 neutrons, while chlorine has an isotope containing 17 protons and 19 neutrons, and argon an isotope with 18 protons and 18 neutrons. These are all isobars, having the same mass number—36, but they all have different chemical properties, due to different numbers of protons in the nucleus and hence different numbers of orbital electrons, which control the chemical properties in each case.

The atom consists principally of empty space, since in the average atom about 99.98% of its mass is concentrated in the nucleus, which usually occupies less than a millionth of a millionth of its volume. The diameter of the nucleus usually ranges between 10^{-13} centimeters and 10^{-12} centimeters, while that of the atom usually ranges between 10^{-8} centimeters and 10^{-7} centimeters. However, since the atom has no definite and rigid boundary, its size cannot be defined with precision, but there is a limit beyond which atoms do not normally approach each other, due to mutual repulsion, and the size of an atom is usually considered to be the volume it occupies,— its shape being spherical,—in a solid, where the atoms touch each other, although this volume varies appreciably in different chemical compounds. The diameters of the atoms do not vary according to their weights, but are not far from the same for all atoms, due to the fact that, in the more complex atoms, the greater attraction exerted by the more highly charged nucleus draws the orbital electrons closer to it. Thus, comparison between helium and uranium, respectively the next to lightest and the heaviest atom existing in nature, shows that, although the uranium atom weighs over fifty times as much as the helium atom, they do not differ greatly as to size,—the uranium atom, in fact, being somewhat the smaller of the two.

	Weight.	Diameter.
Helium.	6.64 x 10^{-24} gram.	3.98 x 10^{-8} centimeter.
Uranium.	3.95 x 10^{-22} gram.	3.44 x 10^{-8} centimeter.

Reference has previously been made to "stable" and "unstable" isotopes. Stable isotopes are those, which, under normal conditions, remain unchanged through an indefinite period of time; while unstable isotopes are those, which, under normal conditions, disintegrate naturally and spontaneously into other isotopes within measureable periods of time. It was formerly thought that the elements were immutable and immortal, but, commencing with the discovery of radioactivity by Becquerel in 1896, of radium and polonium by the

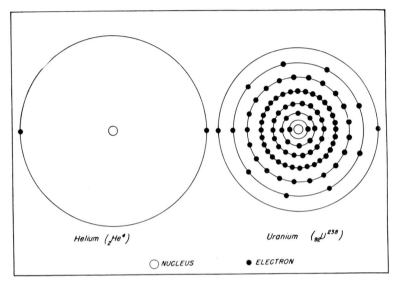

Helium $(_{2}He^{4})$ Uranium $(_{92}U^{238})$

○ *NUCLEUS*   ● *ELECTRON*

FIGURE 1 - 4

Illustrating diagrammatically the atomic structures and comparative sizes of the helium atom $(_{2}He^{4})$ and the uranium atom $(_{92}U^{238})$. Not drawn to scale,— the sizes of the nuclei and electrons being greatly exaggerated, while the shells of the uranium atom are not correctly spaced.

Curies two years later, and of the emission of helium from radium by Ramsey and Soddy in 1903, it has been found that, while most of the natural isotopes are stable under conditions now existing on the Earth's surface, certain of the natural isotopes are engaged in changing spontaneously into other isotopes, and it is possible artificially to produce many other similarly unstable isotopes. The spontaneous disintegration of an unstable isotope is called radio-activity, and results in the expulsion from the nucleus, at intervals, of an apha particle, a beta particle (or a positron), or a gamma ray. An alpha particle, which leaves the nucleus at a speed ranging from 8,800 to 12,800 miles a second, and has a range of from 3 to 11 centimeters in air at normal temperature and pressure, consists of two protons and two neutrons, and therefore is identical with the nucleus of the helium atom and has a double positive electrical charge. The expulsion of an alpha particle from the nucleus of an isotope automatically transmutes it into another isotope, with an atomic number two less and a mass number four less than the original isotope, while two orbital electrons are simultaneously released, to balance the loss of two protons from the nucleus. A beta particle is an electron of nuclear origin, identical with an orbital electron, and therefore carrying a single negative electrical charge. It is expelled at a velocity ranging from about 50,000 miles per second to nearly the speed of light—186,272 miles per second. The expulsion of a beta particle automatically transmutes the original isotope into a new isotope, with the same mass number but an atomic number one greater than the original, while an additional orbital electron is acquired from unattached electrons passing in the vicinity, to balance the additional proton in the nucleus. A positron is the same as a beta particle, but with a positive electrical charge instead of a negative electrical charge. A gamma ray is not a particle, but an electromagnetic radiation of very short wave length, without electrical charge, moving with the speed of light. Artificial isotopes of every known element have been produced, and the great majority are beta particle emitters, with or without accompanying gamma ray radiation. The ability to emit an alpha particle seems to be characteristic of the heavy elements almost exclusively. Since all radiation is emitted by the atomic nucleus, which is not affected by chemical processes or reactions, every radioactive isotope, whether natural or artificial, retains all its radioactive properties in all its chemical combinations and in every physical state, whether in the form of a gas, a liquid or a solid. Natural radioactive disintegration, spontaneously initiated, cannot be accelerated, retarded or arrested by any known means, chemical or physical, within human control.

The radioactivity or spontaneous disintegration of a mass of atoms of any one isotope does not continue, from its inception, at the same rate until all of the atoms have been transmuted, but continuously decreases, according to an exponential curve, called the decay curve. This curve is plotted according to the successive half-lives of the radioactive isotope. The half-life of a radioactive isotope is the time required for half of a given quantity of the isotope to disintegrate into a new isotope. In the same time interval following the initial half-life, half of the remaining substance or one quarter of the original substance will disintegrate; in the same time interval following the second half-life, half of the then remaining substance or one eighth of the original substance will disintegrate; and so on. The decay curve thus established is a physical constant, which is identical for all isotopes, except as to the length of the time factor. While theoretically the length of time required for the complete disintegration of a radioactive substance is infinite, in reality the number of surviving atoms drops with relative rapidity, so that at the end of ten successive half-lives, only about one thousandth of the original atoms remain.

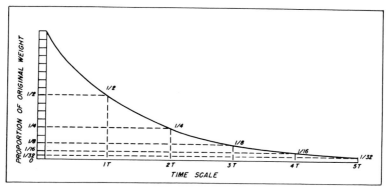

FIGURE 1 - 5

Decay curve of a radioactive element or isotope.

The half-lives of different isotopes differ widely as to length, ranging from a fraction of a second to several billion years. Thus, half-lives as short as 10^{-9} second have been measured, although these are generally transitions in which only a gamma ray is emitted; while, at the other extreme, the half-life of one isotope of uranium ($_{92}U^{238}$) is 4,500,000,000 years. It should be understood that not all of the atoms of a radioactive substance are disintegrating at the same time, but only a fraction of them, determined by the length of the half-life, and the time required for disintegration to take place,— the remaining atoms being unchanged. The disintegration of an unstable atom takes place in an extremely short time,—something like 10^{-18} to 10^{-20} second. So if, for purpose of illustration, it be assumed that a certain unstable isotope has a half-life of one year (31,558,150 seconds), only one sixty-millionth of the atoms composing a mass of this isotope will disintegrate in any one second, on the average, during the first year.

The final product of the radioactive disintegration of any isotope is one or more stable isotopes, and if the first isotope produced in the process is not itself stable, then it in turn will disintegrate, and this process will continue until stable end products are reached. Thus, the disintegration of one isotope of uranium ($_{92}U^{238}$) proceeds through fifteen successive steps, before stable end products are obtained, as per the following table:

Element	Isotope	Atomic No.	Mass No.	Particle Ejected	Range in Air	Half-life Period
Uranium	$_{92}U^{238}$	92	238	Alpha	2.70 cm.	4.5 x 10^9 years
Thorium	$_{90}Th^{234}$	90	234	Beta, gamma		24.1 days
Protactinium	$_{91}Pa^{234}$	91	234	Beta, gamma		1.15 minutes.
Uranium	$_{92}U^{234}$	92	234	Alpha	3.28 cm.	2.6 x 10^5 years.
Thorium	$_{90}Th^{230}$	90	230	Alpha	3.19 cm.	8 x 10^4 years
Radium	$_{88}Ra^{226}$	88	226	Alpha	3.39 cm.	1610 years
Radon	$_{86}Rn^{222}$	86	222	Alpha	4.12 cm.	3.82 days
Polonium	$_{84}Po^{218}$	84	218	Alpha	4.64 cm.	3.05 minutes
Lead	$_{82}Pb^{214}$	82	214	Beta, gamma		26.8 minutes
Bismuth	$_{83}Bi^{214}$	83	214	Beta, gamma (99.96%) Alpha (0.04%)		19.7 minutes
(99.96%) Polonium	$_{84}Po^{214}$	84	214	Alpha	6.97 cm.	1.5 x 10^{-4} sec.
(0.04%) Thallium	$_{81}Tl^{210}$	81	210	Beta		1.32 minutes
Lead	$_{82}Pb^{210}$	82	210	Beta, gamma		22 years
Bismuth	$_{83}Bi^{210}$	83	210	Beta, gamma		5 days
Polonium	$_{84}Po^{210}$	84	210	Alpha	3.92 cm.	139 days
Lead	$_{82}Pb^{206}$	82	206			Stable

The end products consist of one atom of lead ($_{82}Pb^{206}$) and eight alpha particles (helium nuclei), which will capture orbital electrons from unattached electrons passing close by, and thus convert themselves into eight atoms of helium ($_2He^4$). Thus the final result of the disintegration of one ounce of uranium isotope ($_{92}U^{238}$) will be 0.8653 ounce of lead isotope ($_{82}Pb^{206}$) 0.1345 ounce of helium ($_2He^4$) and 0.0002 ounce of radiation.

While a normal atom, with a full complement of orbital electrons, is electrically neutral, such an atom, when containing several electrons, may lose one of its outer orbital electrons, and thus become electrically positive, in which condition the atom is said to be ionized, or it may lose two or more of its outer orbital electrons, and thus acquire two or more positive electrical charges, and be termed doubly or multiply ionized.

In addition to the three principal particles of matter previously described,—the electron, the proton and the neutron,—which are overwhelmingly the most abundant, four other particles,—the positron, the meson, the neutrino and the photon,—have been identified. The positron, which is produced naturally by the impact of cosmic rays on the Earth's atmosphere (See Chapter II, p. 66), and artificially during the disintegration of certain radioactive isotopes, has the same size and mass as the electron and spins on its axis with the same speed, but its electrical charge, which is of exactly the same magnitude as that of the electron, is positive instead of negative. It is very short-lived, because when it encounters an electron, both are simultaneously annihilated, with the formation of two gamma rays instead. Mesons, which are produced naturally by the action of cosmic rays on the Earth's atmosphere and artificially through the impact of very energetic particles on atomic nuclei, are of several kinds. Most of them have masses somewhere between 200 and 300 times that of the electron, but a few are heavier. Some are positively charged and some are negatively charged, each with an electrical charge equal to that of the electron, while some are neutral. Some of them spin on their axes, with an angular momentum the same as that of the electron, while others do not. All mesons are very unstable, disintegrating in a minute fraction of a second, with the production of electrons, neutrinos, other mesons and gamma rays. The neutrino is a particle without mass or electrical charge, moving with the speed of light, while it has an axial spin equal to that of the electron. Photons, which are equivalent to electromagnetic waves, are particles of zero mass, travelling with the velocity of light. Gamma rays are high energy photons.

While an atom is the smallest particle of an element, which can exist, while retaining all the properties of the element, most atoms can exist independently only briefly, and an atom is usually combined with another atom of the same element or with one or more atoms of other elements to form what are called molecules. Thus the molecules of the elements helium (He_1) and neon (Ne_1) contain but one atom each; the molecules of the elements oxygen (O_2) and nitrogen (N_2) contain two atoms each; while ozone (O_3) is an exceptional case of a molecule consisting of three atoms of the same element. Molecules composed of different elements may range in complexity of structure from those with only two atoms each to those containing hundreds of thousands or even millions of atoms, such as some protein and virus molecules. In molecules, the outer electrons of the constituent atoms may encircle, as a whole, all the nuclei of several neighboring atoms, with very complex orbits, forming what are termed "clouds" of electrons.

Molecules exist in three different physical states, as solids, liquids and gases. Solids have been aptly distinguished as possessing both volume and shape, liquids as possessing volume but not shape, and gases as having neither volume nor shape. Liquids and gases are distinguished from solids by the property of fluidity.

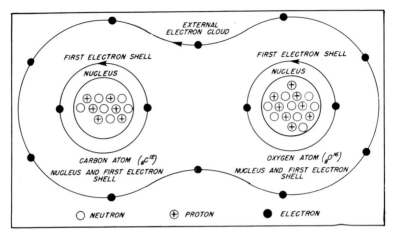

FIGURE 1 - 6

Illustrating diagrammatically the atomic structure of the diatomic molecule, carbon monoxide (CO). Not drawn to scale,—the sizes of the nuclei, neutrons, protons and electrons being greatly exaggerated. (*"Classical And Modern Physics,"* by Harvey E. White, p. 439. Copyright, 1940, by D. Van Nostrand Company, Inc., New York, N. Y.)

There are two kinds of solids: crystalline and amorphous. In crystalline solids the molecules are arranged with a high degree of order and organization, forming what are called space lattices; while in amorphous solids very little order exists. The difference between them in this respect has been compared to the difference between a regiment and a crowd. In both forms of solids, however, the molecules are in contact with one another, and each molecule is so tightly bound by the attractive forces of the surrounding molecules, that it remains for long periods nearly in a constant position relative to the surrounding molecules, although it vibrates within narrow limits about its average position. However, the forces between the molecules are not entirely attractive, because on bringing the molecules too close together a repulsive force of great magnitude sets in, which is responsible for the fact that solids, together with liquids, are nearly incompressible, since the molecules can be made to penetrate one another only with great difficulty. The average amplitude of vibration of a molecule varies with the temperature,—decreasing with lowering temperature until absolute zero (—273.16° C.) is reached, when molecular vibration almost ceases; while, in the other direction, increasing temperature brings about

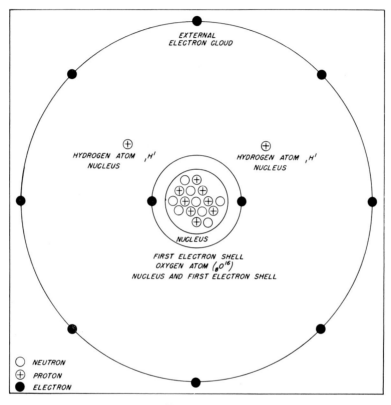

FIGURE 1 - 7

Illustrating diagrammatically the atomic structure of the triatomic molecule, water (H_2O). Not drawn to scale,—the sizes of the nuclei, neutrons, protons and electrons being greatly exaggerated.

increased amplitude of vibration, which forces the molecules further apart, thus causing the expansion of the substance in question. Eventually, when a certain temperature is reached, which differs for different molecules, the vibrations become sufficiently energetic to loosen the bonds, which hold them to surrounding molecules. This temperature is the melting point, at which substances pass from the solid to the liquid state. In crystalline solids, such as metals, the melting point is usually rather sharply defined, and the substance passes rather abruptly from the solid to the liquid state. In amorphous solids, such as glass, on the other hand, the solid may soften some time before it melts, and the melting point is not sharply defined.

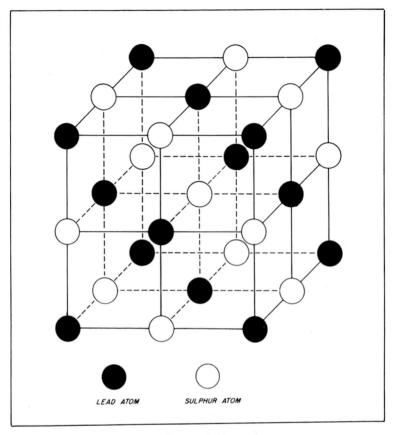

LEAD ATOM   SULPHUR ATOM

FIGURE 1 - 8

Illustrating diagrammatically the atomic structure of a crystal of galena (PbS).
Not drawn to scale,—the sizes of the atoms of lead and sulphur being reduced
considerably.

A simple form of space lattice in a crystalline solid is illustrated
in the accompanying diagram of the cubical structure in a crystal
of galena (PbS), in which a unit cube contains four atoms of lead
and four atoms of sulphur, with the lead and the sulphur atoms
occupying alternate corners of the cube so that atoms of the same
element are never immediate neighbors. In such a galena crystal,
the distance between the centers of adjacent lead and sulphur atoms
amounts to 2.965×10^{-8} centimeters, so that a crystal one inch long
on the side contains nearly a million million million million molecules
and twice as many atoms.

In the liquid state, the molecules are still in contact or almost in contact with each other, but there is greater freedom of movement, since the molecules, although temporarily bound together, are continually changing partners, as it were. As the molecules of a liquid move relatively to one another, frictional forces come into play, and these forces tend to retard the movement of the molecules, creating the phenomenon known as viscosity, which varies with the temperature and the nature of the liquid. A very viscous liquid has many properties in common with a plastic solid. The difference is that any substance, which exhibits sluggish flow under all stresses, at rates somewhat proportional to the stresses, is a viscous liquid, whereas a substance, which does not flow, or flows only slightly, until a certain minimum stress is exceeded, is a plastic solid. On heating, the vibrations of a molecule in a liquid increase, until the vibrations become sufficiently energetic for each molecule to break completely away from all other molecules. This marks the boiling point of the substance, above which the substance is in the vapor or gaseous state.

The molecules of a gas are continually in motion, more or less independently of one another, in random directions, colliding with each other and with the walls of the container, if enclosed. It is the impact of the moving molecules upon the latter which causes a gas to exert pressure. In addition to having a linear motion, a gas molecule also vibrates and rotates on its axis; and for all these motions, the energy is directly proportional to the absolute temperature, and the molecular velocities are directly proportional to the square root of the absolute temperature (the absolute temperature being the temperature measured in degrees centigrade above the absolute zero,—273.16° C.), increasing with rising temperature and decreasing with falling temperature down to the point where the gas is transformed into the liquid state. In the gaseous state, the total number of molecules per unit volume of gas is exactly the same for all substances at the same temperature and pressure (Avogadro's law), and at 0° C. and 760 mm. of mercury pressure (the normal atmospheric pressure at sea-level) this number amounts to 2.7×10^{19} molecules per cubic centimeter. The speed of molecules of different substances, at any certain temperature, however, is not the same, but varies inversely as the square root of their molecular weights. Thus, three of the atmospheric gases,—hydrogen, nitrogen and oxygen,— compare as follows, as to density, average (root mean square) velocity per molecule, and mean free path or average distance travelled per molecule between collisions, at 0° C. and 760 mm. pressure of mercury, in the Earth's atmosphere.

	Molecular weight	Density lbs. per cu. ft.	Average (Root mean square) velocity of molecules	Mean free path of molecules
Hydrogen (H$_2$)	2.016	0.0056	18.4 x 10^4 cm. per sec. (1.144 miles per sec.)	18.3 x 10^{-6} cm.
Nitrogen (N$_2$)	28.016	0.078	4.9 x 10^4 cm. per sec. (0.305 miles per sec.)	9.4 x 10^{-6} cm.
Oxygen (O$_2$)	32.000	0.089	4.6 x 10^4 cm. per sec. (0.286 miles per sec.)	9.9 x 10^{-6} cm.

For hydrogen, this means about 10,000,000,000 collisions per molecule per second, and about half as many for nitrogen and oxygen.

Although a liquid is intermediate in form between a solid and a gas, it is much closer in its physical properties to the former than to the latter. Thus, the density of a liquid is usually within 10% of the solid from which it has been derived, but it is often a thousand times that of its vapor or gas. For example, 18 grams of water occupies 0.0188 liter in the liquid state at 100° C., but the same molecules occupy about 30 liters when changed into a gas at the same temperature, so that the volume occupied by each molecule in the form of a gas is 1600 times as much as it occupied in the liquid state.

CHAPTER TWO

The Constitution of the Universe

The vast, shoreless sea of darkness, in which the Earth spins tirelessly, is almost an empty void, according to our present conception of the nature of matter. If all the matter in the visible Universe were distributed uniformly through the space it occupies, it has been estimated that there would be but one atom of average size in each cubic centimeter; and since a representative atom, such as that of helium, has a diameter of only 3.98×10^{-8} centimeter (not much greater than an hundred millionth of an inch), the total volume of all the atoms existing within a space the size of the Earth, if gathered together, would probably not greatly exceed the size of a golf ball.

Although the Sun and the Moon dominate our sky, their seeming size and importance are due solely to their relative proximity. The Moon, by volume, is only 1/49th as large as the Earth; while the Sun, although it is 1,306,000 times as large as the Earth, and is the source of the light and the heat, which alone make the Earth habitable, is a relatively insignificant part of the Universe. The bright but very minute points of light, which spangle the heavens at night, and which are called the stars, are, with few exceptions, other suns, comparable to our own in average size and general character. They are so remote that their bodies or disks cannot be distinguished. Like distant searchlights, the light, which they emit, serves only to reveal their existence and to disclose their positions.

These faraway suns are termed the "fixed stars," to distinguish them from some 1,500 other stars, which, as planets or satellites, are members of our own Solar System, and which shine only by reflected light, and are relatively so near the Earth that their motion can be detected within periods of a few hours or days. But the fixed stars are by no means stationary, as their name would seem to imply. Instead, they travel at high velocities, of tens and hundreds of miles per second, but they are so remote that they seem to change position very slowly. Sirius, the "Dog-star," which is one of the nearest of our celestial neighbors, moves at a rate that will cause it to cross a space equal to the diameter of the Moon in about 1,400 years; but in the cases of most of the stars, thousands of years must pass before any changes in their positions become noticeable.

The intervals between the stars are of the same order of magnitude as those which separate the Solar System from them, and are so vast that it is more convenient to express them in terms of light-years than in miles. A light-year is the distance that light, travelling at the unvarying rate of 186,272 miles a second, will traverse in a year's time; it approximates 5,880,000,000,000 miles. The distance of 93,000,000 miles, which separates the Earth from the Sun, can be traversed by light in about 8 minutes; but the nearest fixed star, Proxima Centauri, is 4.3 light-years distant, while the most remote celestial objects, which can be perceived through the 100 inch telescope on Mt. Wilson, California,—until recently the largest in existence,—are some 500,000,000 light years distant.*

In the whole celestial sphere, only between 6,000 and 7,000 stars can be distinctly seen by the average eye, under the best conditions of visibility. Each increase in power, through the telescope, adds to this number, until, through the 100 inch telescope, some 1,500,000,000 stars can be registered on photographic plates. Their profusion perhaps can be better appreciated from the fact that within the quadrilateral of bright stars, which forms the bowl of the "Big Dipper" in the constellation of Ursa Major in the northern celestial hemisphere, and which encloses only about a thousandth part of the whole sky, the unaided eye can perceive no more than a dozen faint stars, whereas the telescope reveals 150,000. With a still further increase in telescopic power, it is certain that myriads of other stars, now invisible because of distance or faintness of luminosity, would be disclosed.

The distant suns, which constitute the fixed stars, are by no means uniform in character, but instead vary as to surface temperature, color, luminosity, size, weight, density and surface composition. The surface temperature varies from about 23,000° K.* for the

*FOOTNOTE: Recent measurements indicate that the most remote celestial objects visible through the Mt. Wilson telescope may be twice as far away as previously supposed, or 1,000,000,000 light years distant.

hottest known stars to about 1,700° K. for the coldest visible stars, although there are doubtless some dark, non-luminous stars of still lower temperature.

The color varies with the surface temperature, as follows:

Star Exemplar	Constellation	Color	Surface Temperature
Rigel	Orion	Blue	16,000° K.
Sirius	Canis Major	White	11,000° K.
Procyon	Canis Minor	Pale yellow	8,000° K.
Sun		Yellow	6,000° K.
Arcturus	Boötes	Reddish	3,500° K.
Betelgeuse	Orion	Red	2,700° K.

There is doubtless still another class,—that of dark stars, whose surface temperatures are so low that they are not luminous; for while no such stars have been seen, because stars must emit light to be visible from the Earth, this is the next logical step in the evolution of the stars, as will later be discussed, and the existence of much dark, non-luminous matter in the Universe is well established.

The composition of the outermost layers of the stars can be determined by spectrum analysis, whereby the light coming from the stars is broken up into its component parts, which enables the atomic source of the light to be determined. The nature of the outermost layer in each star depends upon its temperature, and therefore on the degree of excitation of the atoms composing it. In the hottest stars, ionized elements are predominant; with falling temperature the ionized elements tend to disappear and to be replaced by neutral elements; while in the coolest stars the neutral elements decrease in abundance and are supplanted by chemical compounds. In detail, the following sequence is representative of outermost stellar atmospheres, commencing with the hottest stars and ending with the coolest ones:

1. Ionized helium and trebly ionized oxygen and nitrogen.
2. Neutral helium and singly ionized oxygen and nitrogen.
3. Ionized metals appear, such as calcium, magnesium and iron, and hydrogen becomes abundant.

---

*FOOTNOTE: K, for Kelvin, indicates the absolute temperature, measured in degrees centigrade above the absolute zero (—273.16° C.), which is the lowest possible temperature attainable, and the one at which all molecular motion comes to a stand-still.

4. Neutral metals begin to appear, while hydrogen diminishes.
5. Ionized calcium is common, neutral metals become abundant, while hydrogen continues to diminish.
6. Titanium oxide appears and becomes steadily more abundant.
7. Carbon compounds and cyanogen appear.
8. Zirconium oxide appears.

The intrinsic luminosity or real brightness of a star, which depends only on its size and surface temperature, is to be distinguished from its visual or apparent luminosity, which is affected also by its distance and by the existence of any obscuring material between it and the observer. Rigel, which is intrinsically the brightest star known, is 14,000 times more luminous than the Sun, while the least luminous star known has only about 1/11,000th the brightness of the Sun, and therefore is only about 1/150,000,000th as bright as Rigel.

The stars are divided into three classes as to size. The largest stars are termed "giants"; those of intermediate size are called "main sequence" stars; while the smallest are termed "dwarfs." The main sequence stars, of which the Sun is a representative member, although somewhat above the average size, comprise about 5/6th of the whole. The giants constitute the next most numerous class. Their largest member is the star Antares in the constellation Scorpius, which has a diameter greater than that of the orbit of the planet Mars and hence is over 100,000,000 times as large as the Sun, but its weight is only about 30 times that of the Sun, so that it has the extremely low density of 3×10^{-7} as compared with water, amounting to only 1/3,000 that of air at normal temperature and pressure. The dwarfs constitute the smallest class, but this is probably due to the fact that their small size causes low visibility, so that only those comparatively near the Sun are known at the present time. It is possible that in actual numbers they may equal or even exceed the main sequence stars. The smallest dwarf star known is that called Van Maanen's star, which is believed to have a diameter only about three quarters of that of the Earth, but to weigh many thousand times as much, and hence to have a very high density.

In weight, the stars do not exhibit the extreme differences that they do in size. Of those stars, whose weight is known with any degree of accuracy, the heaviest is Star H. D. 1337 (Pearce's star), which is a double star, with one component weighing 36.3 and the other 33.8 times as much as the Sun. However, Plaskett's star (B. D. 6° 1309), which is also a double star, is probably heavier still, although its weight is not known with assurance,—the two components appearing to weigh at least 75 and 63 times as much as the Sun, respectively. Two of the lightest stars known are the components of Kruger 60, which also is a double star,—one component weighing one fourth and the other one fifth that of the Sun.

On the average, the giant stars are the least dense, as illustrated in the case of Antares. The main sequence stars have greater densities, usually somewhere in the vicinity of that of water. Some of the dwarf stars have extraordinarily high densities, as illustrated by the star known as the Companion of Sirius or Sirius B. Sirius, in the constellation Canis Major, popularly known as the "Dog-Star," is distant about 8.65 light years from the Earth, and is a double star, consisting of a large component, which is the brightest fixed star in the sky, known as Sirius A, and a small, faint component, known as Sirius B. The two revolve about their common center of gravity, at a distance apart about 20 times that which separates the Sun from the Earth, in a period of 49 years. Their individual characteristics, as compared with the Sun and with each other, are as follows:

	Sun	Sirius A	Sirius B
Luminosity (Sun : 1)	1	26.3	0.0026
Surface temperature	6,000° K.	11,000° K.	8,000° K.
Diameter (miles)	865,400	1,374,000	23,400
Mass (Earth : 1)	333,420	816,880	283,400
Density (Water : 1)	1.41	0.88	61,000

An outstanding feature of this ill-assorted pair of stars, of which Sirius A belongs to the main sequence while Sirius B is a dwarf star, is the enormous disparity between their densities, and the remarkable fact that the density of Sirius B is 61,000 times that of water, or over 2,700 times that of osmium, the heaviest metal known in the Earth's crust, so that one cubic inch of the material in Sirius B weighs somewhat more than a ton. However, this is not an isolated instance, as other dwarf stars are known with seemingly abnormally high densities. Thus the star 40 Eridani B, which is one of a binary system, has a surface temperature of 11,000° K., a diameter of about 16,500 miles, a mass about 147,000 times that of the Earth, and a density of about 64,000 as compared with water, closely approaching that of Sirius B.

There is no sharp separation or distinction between the three classes of stars, for giants grade into main sequence stars and the latter into dwarfs. The comparative features of three representative stars of somewhat different type are illustrated as follows:

Star	Mass (Sun:1)	Mean Density (Water:1)	Surface Temp.	Color	Luminosity (Sun:1)
Algol	4.3	0.15	12,000° K.	White	150.
Sun	1.0	1.41	6,000° K.	Yellow	1.
Kruger 60	0.27	9.1	3,000° K.	Red	0.001

While most of the stars are single, like the Sun, a considerable number are multiple stars, comprising two or more components. Double or binary stars, of which examples have previously been referred to, are by far the most common, but some stars of this class are triple while a few are quadruple.

Most of the stars, like the Sun, shine with a fairly steady and uniform light, but probably about 5% of all the stars change more or less in brightness, and are known as variable stars. The bright star Algol in the constellation Perseus consists of a pair of stars very close together, which lie nearly in the same plane as the line of sight from the Earth, and hence at regular intervals eclipse each other nearly completely, thus temporarily reducing the amount of light which the Earth receives from them. Such stars are called eclipsing variables.

Stars of another type, whose light emission varies, but which are not eclipsing variables, are called Cepheid variables, after the type star of the class, Delta Cephei. The light from this star, which is single, fluctuates regularly or pulsates, increasing about double in luminosity and then returning to its original condition, the complete cycle consuming five and a third days. The pulsation is not symmetrical, as the increase from minimum to maximum light emission takes only one fourth of the entire period, the remainder being consumed in the return to minimum. The periods of Cepheid variables range from a few hours to a few weeks, and in general the greater the luminosity of a star of this class, the longer the period. Nearly all of the Cepheid variables are giant stars, usually white or yellow in color, ranging from 100 to 10,000 times the Sun's luminosity. Delta Cephei itself is believed to have nine times the Sun's mass. The light variation in this type of star appears to be due to a periodic expansion and contraction of the star in size, accompanied by an increase and decrease in its surface temperature; but the expansion amounts to only a fraction of the star's diameter.

A third type of periodic variable star is called a long-period variable,—the periods ranging from a few weeks to a few years, but being in the vicinity of 300 days for the majority of stars of this class. While resembling the Cepheid variables in general, the long-period variables do not repeat themselves with the clock-like precision of the two classes previously described, but tend to fluctuate irregularly in both period and amplitude. Nearly all of the stars of this class are giants like the Cepheids, but unlike them they are mostly red in color. The type star Mira in the constellation Cetus is believed to have 300 times the diameter of the Sun.

A fourth type of variable stars is not periodic but fluctuates irregularly and unsystematically in luminosity; while a fifth type, called a temporary star or "nova," is one which, without warning, abruptly and rapidly expands many times in brightness, but usually does so only once, without repetition,—at least within the period of observation. Accompanying the increase in size and brightness of a nova are significant changes in the star's spectrum, commencing with lines due to ionized atoms of such elements as calcium, iron and titanium, and finishing with those due to ionized atoms of oxygen, nitrogen and helium,—in other words, indicating a great increase in temperature. The rise to maximum size and luminosity is exceedingly swift, usually taking place in not more than two or three days, but after attaining its maximum the typical nova begins almost immediately to fade, the fall at first being rapid, then gradually slackening until, in from ten to twenty years, the star returns to its former size and brightness. Novae are rarely known to repeat. Only a few novae, probably between ten and twenty, occur each year. The "Star of Bethlehem" may have been a nova.

To the naked eye, the stars appear to be distributed throughout the sky very unevenly. The only system apparent has to do with the irregular band of soft, misty light, which encircles the firmament like a girdle, dividing it into two nearly equal halves, and which is called by the appropriate name of the "Milky Way." It is of irregular width and outline, differs in brightness in different sections, and in places contains dark patches. For nearly a third of its length it is divided into two bands by a central dark zone of irregular width. The telescope shows the Milky Way to be composed chiefly of stars, most of which are so remote that they cannot be individually distinguished by the naked eye, and it is only the effect of their massed illumination that is perceived. Along the Milky Way the stars are crowded in such throngs as to be beyond counting, but with departure to one side or the other they become less abundant and are scarcest of all in the parts of the sky most distant from it.

The Milky Way consists of a vast assemblage of stars, comprising not only all the fixed stars in the heavens, that are visible to the naked eye, but also all of the fixed stars that can be distinguished by telescopes other than those of highest power. This star assemblage is called the galactic system, and appears to have the shape of a flattened disk, somewhat like a thin watch. Its appearance from the Earth is due to the fact that it is viewed edgeways from a point within it,—the Sun being a member of this system; and the circumstance that the Milky Way divides the sky almost equally in halves indicates that the Sun is situated nearly along the median plane of this flattened disk. The dimensions of the galactic system are tremendous. It is believed to have a diameter of about 100,000 light years and a thickness of from 5,000 to 10,000 light years. It rotates about an axis, which is at right angles to its greatest extension, so that it acts like a greatly flattened top. The speeds of the stars, which compose the system, vary with distance from the axis,—the nearer stars moving faster than the more remote ones. The Sun appears to lie about 30,000 light years or two thirds of the distance from its center to its periphery, at which point the Sun, moving at a speed of about 185 miles per second in its orbit, would complete a revolution in about 190,000,000 years.

The number of stars in the galactic system is beyond counting, because in some portions of the Milky Way they appear so crowded as to defy separation, while elsewhere the view is obscured by clouds of dark nebulosity, behind which doubtless many stars are hidden. However, by extrapolating from the number of stars visible through the telescope into the probable extension of the system beyond the limits of visibility, the population of the galactic system has been estimated at about 100,000,000,000 stars of average weight somewhat smaller than the Sun.

Other occupants of the sky, besides stars, are the nebulae, which, as their Latin name suggests, are cloudy masses, both luminous and dark. Of the luminous nebulae, some prove, under high telescopic power, to consist of aggregates of stars, so far distant that ordinarily their massed light merges into a blur, while other luminous nebulae cannot be resolved into stars, but apparently consist of clouds of dust or gas, some of which are illuminated by stars behind them or enmeshed in them, while others appear to be self-

luminous. The nebulae are divided, as to location, into those within
the galactic system, and those without it,—the latter being called
extra-galactic.

Most of the luminous galactic nebulae are irregular in shape
and indefinite in outline, and consist, either of clouds of very fine
particles of cosmic dust, or of very tenuous masses of gas,—both
of which, in most cases, are made visible by illumination furnished
by nearby stars behind them or enclosed in them, although some

Mount Wilson and Palomar Observatories.

PLATE I.   NGC 6514 (Messier 20) "Trifid" Nebula in the constellation Sagittarius.

Mount Wilson and Palomar Observatories.

PLATE II.   NGC 6992 Filamentary Nebula in the constellation Cygnus.

gaseous nebulae of this nature appear to be self-luminous, due
to excitation of the atoms or molecules composing them by radiation of some sort emitted from neighboring stars of very high
temperature. A special type of luminous galactic nebula, small in
size, globular in shape and gaseous in composition, is called a planetary nebula. In almost every instance of this nature, a faint star, blue
in color and of high temperature, can be seen, occupying the center
of the nebula and apparently furnishing the illumination that reveals

it. This association suggests that the star in question had passed through an earlier nova stage, and that the nebula represents a spherical envelope of gas, formed at the time of maximum expansion, which has lagged behind the star in its subsequent return to normalcy. More than a hundred such planetary nebulae have been recognized. Dark nebulae consist of clouds of very fine solid particles of cosmic dust, too thick for the light of the stars behind them to

Mount Wilson and Palomar Observatories.

PLATE III.   NGC 3587 (Messier 97) "Owl" Planetary Nebula in the constellation Ursa Major.

Mount Wilson and Palomar Observatories.

PLATE IV.   IC 434 (Barnard 33)   "Horsehead" Dark Nebula in the constellation Orion.

penetrate through them; but this thickness need not be great and probably never is, since small thicknesses of smoke or steam in the atmosphere of the Earth are capable of completely obscuring the Sun. Both the luminous and dark nebulae are moving and changing shape, although seemingly very slowly.

The extra-galactic nebulae are of quite different nature. As their name suggests, they lie entirely without the galactic system, and hence none can be seen by looking along the Milky Way. It is only by gazing in other directions, through the thin scattering of stars that constitute the portion of the galactic system in the general neighborhood of the Sun, that they can be perceived. In these

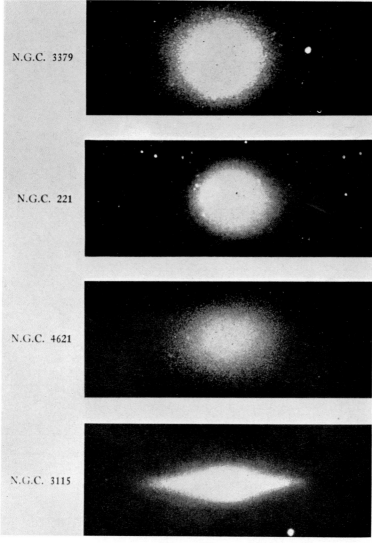

N.G.C. 3379

N.G.C. 221

N.G.C. 4621

N.G.C. 3115

Mount Wilson and Palomar Observatories.

PLATE V-1

A sequence of nebulae, arranged in order of increasing flatness; viewed edge-on.

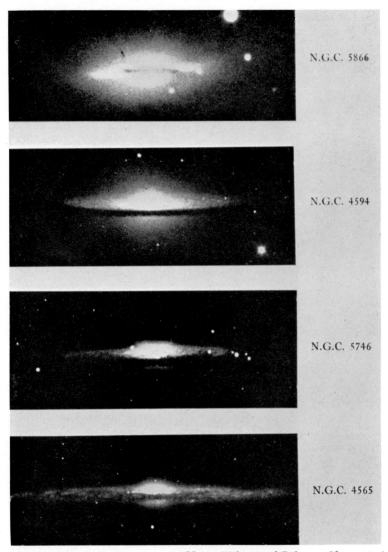

N.G.C. 5866

N.G.C. 4594

N.G.C. 5746

N.G.C. 4565

Mount Wilson and Palomar Observatories.

PLATE V-2

A sequence of nebulae, arranged in order of increasing flatness; viewed edge-on.

directions, they occur in all parts of the sky, but appear in greatest numbers at right angles to the plane of the galactic system, probably because there is least interference with extra-galactic visibility in such direction. The extra-galactic nebulae usually possess somewhat sharper and more definite outlines and more symmetrical shapes than the irregular cloudy and wispy masses, that form most of the galactic nebulae; and they vary in shape from spherical masses, through gradually flattening spheroids, to disk-like shapes,—the latter, when viewed broadside or obliquely, always proving to be spiral in structure.

In some of the nearer extra-galactic nebulae, under the highest telescopic powers, stars can be perceived, including Cepheid variables and novae, together with irregular luminous and dark nebulous clouds, entirely similar to those in the galactic system. From this fact it is deduced that these so-called extra-galactic nebulae are themselves individual and separate galactic systems, similar in general to that constituting the Milky Way; while conversely the Milky Way galactic system is spirally discoid in shape, comparable in all essential respects to those analogous forms of the distant galactic systems, which the telescope reveals. In the course of further discussion, therefore, the term nebula will be reserved for those irregular cloudy bodies of gas and cosmic dust, luminous and non-luminous, which are probably features of all galactic systems, as well as of the Milky Way system, while the term galactic systems will be simplified to galaxies.

The galaxies have sometimes been called "island universes," because of the fact that the Milky Way galaxy was formerly supposed to constitute the entire Universe, while they have sometimes been called "star cities," because all of the stars seem to be confined to them, and none are known to exist in intergalactic space. The aptness of the term "star-cities" will be realized by anybody, who has viewed an earthly city by night, from an elevated point in an outlying residential district. The individual house and street lights near at hand, which can be readily distinguished, compare to those stars of the Milky Way galaxy, which are individually visible to the naked eye. Further away horizontally in all directions the city lights become smaller, more numerous and closer together, until at some distance they merge and coalesce into a general illumination, in which the component lights can be distinguished only by a field glass; this corresponds to the Milky Way. Over the central business section, which is more highly lighted, there rises a low, luminous dome, which is similar to the central part of a spiral galaxy, viewed edgewise. Looking beyond the city into the dark surrounding country-side, there are visible here and there small luminous clots,

Mount Wilson and Palomar Observatories.

PLATE VI.   NGC 1300.   Spiral Nebula in the constellation Eridanus.

which are other towns and cities, so far removed that their lights fuse into a single glow; these would correspond to other distant galaxies.

Those galaxies, which are in the form of spiral disks, occur in all attitudes, ranging from broadside, or at right angles to the line of sight from the Earth, to edgewise, or in the direction of the line of sight, with all degrees of intermediate postures, in which they appear elliptical. Their spiral structure, which is best revealed when they lie broadside, or at right angles to the line of sight from the Earth, resembles somewhat a rotating pin-wheel, but with an important and significant difference. A spiral galaxy has a hub or central nucleus, which is more luminous than the remainder of the galaxy, but, while a pinwheel discharges sparks from all points around the periphery of its hub, a typical spiral galaxy shows only two arms, emerging from its hub at diametrically opposite points,— these arms being more or less closely coiled or wrapped around the

Mount Wilson and Palomar Observatories.

PLATE VII. NGC 3031 (Messier 81) Spiral Nebula in the constellation Ursa Major.

Mount Wilson and Palomar Observatories.

PLATE VIII.   NGC 5364   Spiral Nebula in the constellation Virgo.

hub, as per the sequence shown in Plates VI to X, inclusive. Many
of the spiral galaxies have been proved to be rotating,—the
hubs faster than the arms, which accounts for the arms trailing
after them,—and it is probable that all of them rotate. The arms of
the spiral galaxies are not uniform in thickness throughout their
length, but are usually marked at irregular intervals by clots or
expansions, where the arms are wider and brighter than elsewhere,
probably constituting star clusters. In some of the nearer spiral

galaxies, individual stars can be distinguished in the arms, and also, but less commonly, in the hubs. When viewed edgewise, a spiral galaxy appears as a short, straight bar of light, bulging somewhat on each side of its center, and often divided lengthwise by a central dark band, similar to that which divides the Milky Way galaxy lengthwise for nearly a third of its length. The dark band in such case evidently consists of non-luminous solid particles,—not gas, because in such case it would be transparent,—lying in the plane of the spiral galaxy and extending on all sides beyond its luminous area.

Mount Wilson and Palomar Observatories.

PLATE IX.   NGC 628 (Messier 74)   Spiral Nebula in the constellation Pisces

Mount Wilson and Palomar Observatories.

PLATE X. NGC 5194 (Messier 51) Spiral Nebula in the constellation Canes Venatici, with satellite Nebula NGC 5195.

The galaxies vary considerably in size, ranging in diameter from 100,000 light years to less than 1,000 light years. Their distribution through space, while fairly uniform as a whole, is irregular in detail, as there is a tendency for them to gather into groups and clusters, some of which latter contain over 500 galaxies. The Milky Way galaxy is a member of a small cluster, about 1,000,000 light years in diameter, containing two giant spiral galaxies (Milky Way and Andromeda), one medium sized spiral galaxy (Triangulum), four dwarf elliptical galaxies, six irregular star clouds, and over a hundred globular star clusters. The Andromeda spiral galaxy is of special interest, because it is believed to be nearly a twin of the Milky Way spiral galaxy in size, shape and character, and thus provides a means of showing what the latter probably looks like, when viewed from the same distance and at the same angle. The

Mount Wilson and Palomar Observatories.

PLATE XI. NGC 4565 Spiral Nebula (edge-on) in the constellation Coma Berenices.

Mount Wilson and Palomar Observatories.

PLATE XII. NGC 224 (Messier 31) Great Spiral Nebula in the constellation
Andromeda, with satellite nebulae NGC 205 and NGC 221.

Andromeda galaxy lies oblique to the line of sight, at an angle
of about 15° between that and its plane. It is distant about 750,000
light years from the Earth, is about 80,000 light years in diameter,
has a mass equivalent to about 95,000,000,000 Suns, and its hub or
center rotates once in 11,000,000 years and its periphery once in
92,000,000 years. Under the highest telescopic power its nebulous
appearance at lower powers dissolves into masses of faint stars, in

which Cepheid variables, novae, supergiant stars and ordinary stars can be distinguished, accompanied by luminous and dark nebulosity, so that it is entirely similar to the Milky Way galaxy, and is probably representative of the spiral galaxies as a whole, except for being one of the largest. The Milky Way galaxy, as described on page 28, is believed to be somewhat larger still. The Triangulum spiral galaxy, which is distant about 720,000 light years from the Earth, has a diameter of about 13,000 light years, a mass of about 1,700,000,000 Suns, and its center or hub rotates once in 59,000,000 years and its periphery once in 200,000,000 years. Under high telescopic power, its nebulous appearance is transformed into masses of stars. The

Mount Wilson and Palomar Observatories.

PLATE XIII. NGC 205 Nebula in the constellation Andromeda, a satellite of the great nebula NGC 224, showing resolution into stars.

Mount Wilson and Palomar Observatories.

PLATE XIV.   NGC 6205 (Messier 13)   Globular star cluster in the constellation
Hercules.

Triangulum galaxy is probably typical of the average spiral galaxy,
as to size.

The four dwarf elliptical galaxies all lie in the vicinity of the
Andromeda galaxy, and they too can be resolved into stars, under
high telescopic power. The six irregular star clouds are best represented by the two, which are the biggest and the nearest to the
Earth,—the Large and Small Magellanic Clouds. The Large Magel-

lanic Cloud is 75,000 light years distant from the Earth, and is 10,000 light years in diameter, while the Small Magellanic Cloud is 84,000 light years distant from the Earth and has about half the diameter of its companion. The Small Cloud is estimated to contain over 500,000 stars, and the Large Cloud to have a proportionately greater star population. The globular star clusters consist of spheroidal groups of relatively closely spaced stars, containing from a few

Mount Wilson and Palomar Observatories.

PLATE XV. Part of cluster of nebulae in the constellation Coma Berenices, distant about 40,000,000 light years.

thousand to several hundred thousand individual stars. About 100 globular star clusters, lying from 10,000 light years to 250,000 light years distant from the Earth, surround the Milky Way galaxy—although outside of it—in such a manner and distribution as to suggest some relationship to it. Globular star clusters accompany the Andromeda galaxy also. The direction of movement and speed of the Sun in its orbit around the center of the Milky Way galaxy cause the Andromeda and Triangulum galaxies to appear to be approaching the Milky Way galaxy, and the Large and Small Magellanic Clouds to appear to be receding from it, at comparable velocities. The irregular star clouds and the globular star clusters are themselves galaxies, similar in origin and general nature to the large spherical, elliptical and spiral galaxies, and differing from them only as to size and details of organization. Of the galaxies further distant than those of the Milky Way cluster, only the giant and medium-sized galaxies—about 80% of which are spiral—can be perceived through the telescope, and in only the nearest of them can stars be distinguished. Probably all of them, however, are accompanied by unseen dwarf galaxies, star clouds and globular star clusters, so that the star population of the Universe is doubtless much larger than the telescopic evidence indicates.

From what has gone before, a general picture of the known Universe can now be constructed. The dimensions of this known Universe are determined by the distance to which it can be explored telescopically,—about 500,000,000 light years, through the 100 inch telescope of the Mt. Wilson observatory in southern California,—and hence it constitutes a sphere of this radius. These are not the limits of the Universe itself, because, so far as can be determined, the galaxies extend up to the outer limit of visibility without perceptible thinning in their spacing, and obviously must continue for

FOOTNOTE: The dimensions of the known visible Universe, above stated, have recently been doubled by the correspondingly increased range of the lately installed 200 inch telescope of the Palomar observatory in southern California. Observations through this telescope have shown that the further depths of space thus revealed are also thickly populated by galaxies, and have disclosed no approach to the actual limits of the Universe. Furthermore, recent astronomical remeasurements of space have revealed that stellar distances outside of the Milky Way may be about double what they were formerly supposed to be, and hence that the radius of the known Universe, instead of being about 1,000,000,000 light years, as above, per the Palomar observatory, may be actually about 2,000,000,000 light years. In such case, therefore, all measurements of stellar distances outside of the Milky Way, quoted in this chapter, should be doubled.

an unknown distance beyond. The spherical visible Universe of these dimensions,—which somewhat resembles the sphere of illumination surrounding an isolated street lamp in a fog,—is occupied by an estimated hundred million galaxies of giant and medium size, which vary in shape from spheres to spiral disks, with all intermediate forms, and whose average distance from one another, center to center, is of the order of two million light years.

The galaxies occupying this visible Universe are not stationary, nor are they, like the stars constituting a galaxy, revolving about their common center of gravity. Instead, they all appear to be dispersing, receding from the Earth and from each other at speeds, which seem to be the faster the more distant they are. As an example of the high speeds attained, one group of galaxies, estimated to be about 360 million light years distant, seems to be receding at a velocity of about 38,000 miles per second, or a little over 1/5th the velocity of light.

The conclusion that the galaxies are dispersing is deduced from the fact that the spectra of the galaxies are shifted from their proper positions towards the red end of the spectrum, or that of the light-waves of longer wave-length and lower frequency of vibration,—the so-called Doppler effect, which happens when a luminous object is moving away from the observer. It is analogous to the fact that a locomotive whistle becomes shriller, when it is approaching, because the sound waves are crowded closer together, and becomes deeper toned, when it is departing, because the sound pulses are further apart.

Three hypotheses have been proposed in explanation of this phenomenon. The first is that the entire Universe is expanding uniformly, somewhat like an inflating balloon, thereby causing the distances separating the galaxies to increase, although the latter themselves are not actually in motion. This hypothesis lacks proof, and is not consistent with other phenomena of the Universe. The second hypothesis is that light deteriorates, as it were, while travel-ling long distances,—the frequency of the light beam decreasing and thus shifting towards the red end of the spectrum. This hypo-thesis also lacks supporting evidence and has few adherents. The third hypothesis is that what appears to be taking place is actually happening: the galaxies themselves are in motion and are dispersing through space at high speed from some initial place of origin as yet undetermined. This hypothesis is supported by several lines of evidence, to be later discussed, and seems to be the most plausible of the three.

There are two principal hypotheses as to the origin of the Universe: one that it has evolved and is still evolving from simpler forms of matter to more complex forms of matter, which may be called the Evolutionary Hypothesis; the other that it has degenerated and is still degenerating from more complex forms of matter to simpler forms of matter, which may be called the Devolutionary Hypothesis.

The Evolutionary Hypothesis assumes that matter was originally distributed somewhat uniformly throughout space in the form of individual atoms, but provides no explanation of how this situation originated. These atoms are supposed to have been in motion in random directions, in the course of which they eventually encountered one another, and became attached to each other by means of their mutual attraction, thus forming molecules; while these molecules, in turn, slowly aggregated into gaseous masses, which eventually developed into liquid and solid bodies. An objection to this theory is that, considering the extreme dispersion of such atoms through space, and their very sluggish motion, as might be expected at the average temperature of the Universe, which is only a few degrees above the absolute zero, the chances for encounter and junction of the atoms would seem to be so remote as to be negligible. A further objection is that the molecules, when thus formed, could assemble into aggregates only by means of their individual gravitational attraction, which is so excessively weak that, in the Earth's atmosphere, the molecules act like perfectly elastic spheres, rebounding from collisions with no loss of velocity, and never tending to form aggregates. The primitive molecules would be expected to act similarly. Nature supplies no evidence in support of this hypothesis, for many known cases occur on the Earth, where complex atoms spontaneously disintegrate into simpler ones, but none where simpler atoms integrate into more complex ones,—other than temporarily, perhaps. The Evolutionary Hypothesis is weakened by many unexplained inconsistencies, such as why the spiral galaxies each have two arms instead of being perfect disks, and why the galaxies appear to be dispersing at high speeds.

The most formidable objection to the Evolutionary Hypothesis, however, is that it is inconsistent with one of the physical laws of the Universe, known as the Second Law of Thermodynamics, and also with another law, consequent upon the preceding, known as the Law of the Degradation of Energy. The Second Law of Thermodynamics states simply that heat naturally flows from a body of higher temperature to a body of lower temperature, but never in the reverse direction. The consequence of this law is that in Nature some things can be done, which can never be completely undone, thus creating a constant and irreversible drift in one direction. There are two fundamentally different types of energy: mechanical energy, the higher form; and heat, the lower form. Mechanical energy can be transformed into its exact energy equivalent in heat, but heat cannot be completely transformed back into mechanical energy. There has been no loss of energy in the latter process, but some portion of this energy has become "inert," as it were, being no longer available for the performance of work. The measure of this "inertness" is called entropy; and in the Universe entropy is always increasing and never decreasing. Motion is constantly being transformed into heat and matter into radiation, but there is no exactly equivalent reverse process. This leads, therefore, to the Law of the Degradation of Energy, which states that energy is ever being permanently transformed from higher states into lower states, and that this process will continue inexorably until all active or potentially active energy has been transformed into "inert" and unavailable energy.

An illustration sometimes used to show how something can be done that can never be undone is afforded when a deck of cards, properly arranged in suits and sequences, is shuffled. The first shuffle upsets this organization, and subsequent shuffles further destroy it, until a point is soon reached where the disorganization is complete and no further shuffling will increase it. This disorganization is permanent, for although now and then in billions of subsequent shuffles chance might happen to restore the original arrangement of the cards, it would be only transitory and would again be destroyed by succeeding shuffles. In other words, in Nature organization can be changed into disorganization, but the reverse process cannot take place, without the intervention of some exterior agency. Consequently, according to the physical laws, which seem to govern it, this highly organized Universe can degenerate into Chaos, but such a Universe cannot be evolved out of Chaos, as assumed by the Evolutionary Hypothesis. The Universe, as we perceive it, is like a clock, which has been wound and is now running down, without any perceptible provision for its rewinding. Therefore, unless and until the Second Law of Thermodynamics and its corollary, the Law of the Degradation of Energy, are disproved or shown not to be of universal and perpetual application,—neither of which has yet been done,—they are fatal to the validity of the Evolutionary Hypothesis.

The Devolutionary Hypothesis,—so designated because devolution means degeneration, which is the general cosmogonic process, that it advocates,—assumes that at some time in the far distant past all of the matter constituting the Universe was aggregated together into one gigantic body, known as the Primordial Mass, probably some thousands of millions of miles in diameter. Under the influence of gravity, the interior of this Primordial Mass, whether composed of gases, viscous liquids or plastic solids, must have been compressed to a density far exceeding anything known or possible on the Earth. At some far remote time in the past, this Primordial Mass is assumed to have been explosively disrupted,—possibly because the atoms in its center were so crowded together that they encroached upon one another to such an extent as to set up a destructive chain reaction, which released the enormous energy stored in the atomic nuclei. This explosion is assumed to have caused the Primordial Mass to disintegrate into an immense number of fragments, large and small, accompanied by much lesser debris ranging down to atomic size. In a quarry blast, to which this explosion may be compared, the fragments near the focal point must shove outwardly before them those fragments, which are further distant, thereby increasing the speed of the outer fragments above that of the inner fragments,— the result being progressively greater velocity with position of the fragments outwardly from the focal point of the explosion. In such a situation, all the fragments would actually be separating from one another, even where they were moving in the same general direction. The same would be true of the assumed explosion of the Primordial Mass, as illustrated in Figure 2 - 1, and the rate of speed at which any two fragments of this mass would appear to be separating, as viewed from the Earth, would depend on their respective velocities and respective directions of flight. The time when the explosion took place can be calculated approximately from the present distance of any certain galaxy from the Milky Way galaxy (in which the Earth, the point of observation, is located) and the speed at which it seems to be receding, thus determining how long ago both were parts of the Primordial Mass. Five galaxies, thus investigated, lying at various distances and in various directions, have supplied the

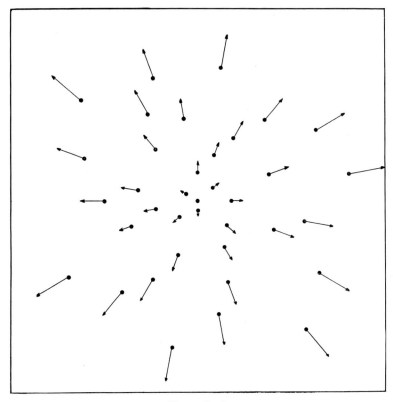

FIGURE 2 - 1

Illustrating dispersal of fragments of an explosively disrupted Primordial Mass,
—the lengths of the arrows indicating the relative speeds. (*"Classical and
Modern Physics,"* p. 667, by Harvey E. White. Copyrighted 1940, D. Van
Nostrand Company, Inc., New York, N. Y.)

following figures. The velocities are not actual, but simply the
difference, in each case, between the component of the velocity of
the galaxy and the component of the velocity of the Earth, measured
along the line of sight; while the distances indicated are not the
present distances between the Earth and the galaxies in question,
but instead are the distances between the present position of the
Earth and the positions of the galaxies when the light now arriving
from them started to leave them, so that it is necessary to add to the
travel time calculated on the basis of the indicated distances the
travel time of the light from the galaxies to the Earth.

It will be noted that not only do the more distant galaxies seem
to be departing at much higher speeds than the nearer ones, but

| | Velocity away from the Earth | | | | |
Galaxy	Miles per sec.	Light years per year	Distance in light years	Travel time in years	Adjusted travel time in years
NGC 4473 Virgo Cluster	1,300	.00698	5,850,000	838,000,000	843,850,000
NGC 379 Pisces Group	3,300	.01772	23,000,000	1,298,000,000	1,321,000,000
Nebula in Ursa Major Cluster	9,200	.04939	82,000,000	1,660,000,000	1,742,000,000
Nebula in Gemini Cluster	13,800	.07408	133,000,000	1,794,000,000	1,927,000,000
Nebula in Boötes Cluster	23,400	.12562	228,000,000	1,815,000,000	2,043,000,000

they also appear to have been longer on their way. The latter discrepancies may be caused by some constant error, that is a function of distance, in the interpretation of the significance of the amount of the red shift; or they may indicate that the disintegration of the Primordial Mass may not have originated all at one time, so that all the fragments commenced to move simultaneously, but that it may have been progressive from the periphery inward, so that there may have been time intervals between the departure of the different fragments,—those nearer the periphery being expelled earlier than those nearer the center. The results previously shown suggest an age of the Universe, as measured from the commencement of the disruption of the Primordial Mass, of somewhere about 2,000,000,000 years; but since more distant galaxies are known to exist within the visible Universe beyond the furthest galaxy shown in the preceding table,—not to mention galaxies probably lying beyond the limits of the visible Universe,—and since such more distant galaxies, if investigated, would probably seem to be moving at still higher speeds and to have been still longer on their way, the possible age of the Universe may extend up to 4,000,000,000 years or more.

The fragments produced by the explosive disintegration of the Primordial Mass, upon release from confinement under great pressure within it, appear, in their turn, to have been explosively disrupted, and this process seems to have continued until fragments sufficiently small to possess relative stability and to resist further disintegration were produced. These subsequently developed into stars, under a process later described, and thus the galaxies of stars were formed.

In the transformation of the large fragments of the Primordial Mass into galaxies of stars, the forms assumed by the galaxies would depend chiefly on whether or not the fragments were rotating, immediately after parting from the Primordial Mass, and, if so, the speed of such rotation. In a quarry explosion, it may be observed that some of the rock fragments are hurled outwardly without rotating, while others, due to being jostled at the inception of their flight, acquire a spinning motion and roll when they land. Similarly, a large fragment of the Primordial Mass, if not rotating, would tend to develop into a nearly spherical galaxy of stars, while if rotating with some rapidity it would tend, because of centrifugal force, to develop into a disk-shaped galaxy of stars. Fragments in slow rotation would tend to develop into intermediate forms, such as flattened spheroids. As would be expected, the disk-shaped spiral galaxies all are rotating, so far as has been determined, but they exhibit certain peculiarities of form, which indicate that other influences, besides centrifugal force, had a hand in their development. If the spiral form was due simply to centrifugal force, they should be throwing matter off all around their periphery, like the sparks from a pin-wheel or the mud from the rim of a wheel. Instead, however, all of them—or nearly all of them—exhibit two curved radiating arms, which depart from the hub or center at diametrically opposite points. Sometimes the arms are loosely coiled about the hub; sometimes they are closely coiled; and sometimes they are so tightly coiled as to appear like annular rings. Such a type of spiral disk can be formed only in one way, by the attraction of a neighboring body of comparable or greater mass, which produces tidal effects. As shown on the accompanying illustration, the gravitational forces in a non-rotating, unattracted body are of equal strength at all localities on its surface and point towards its center. But when such a body is subject to the attraction of a nearby body of similar or greater mass, this nearby attracting body tends to attract the side of the attracted body nearest to it more than its center and its center more than the diametrically opposite side, because of greater nearness in each case, thus weakening the force of gravity at these two opposite sides, and creating forces pointing towards the attracting body on the near side of the attracted body and away from the attracting body on the far side of the attracted body. At points on

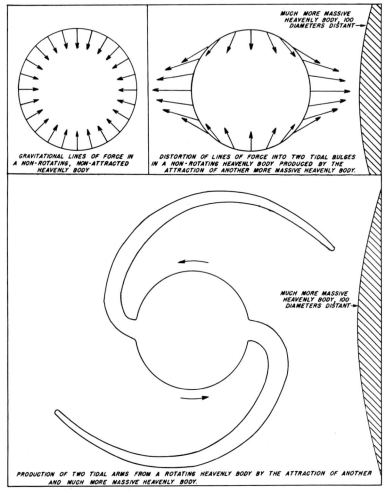

GRAVITATIONAL LINES OF FORCE IN
A NON-ROTATING, NON-ATTRACTED
HEAVENLY BODY

MUCH MORE MASSIVE
HEAVENLY BODY, 100
DIAMETERS DISTANT→

DISTORTION OF LINES OF FORCE INTO TWO TIDAL BULGES
IN A NON-ROTATING HEAVENLY BODY PRODUCED BY THE
ATTRACTION OF ANOTHER MORE MASSIVE HEAVENLY BODY.

MUCH MORE MASSIVE
HEAVENLY BODY, 100
DIAMETERS DISTANT→

PRODUCTION OF TWO TIDAL ARMS FROM A ROTATING HEAVENLY BODY BY THE ATTRACTION OF ANOTHER
AND MUCH MORE MASSIVE HEAVENLY BODY.

FIGURE 2 - 2

Illustrating diagrammatically the mode of formation of a spiral galaxy.

the surface of the attracted body other than in a direct line between its center and that of the attracting body, the effect will be proportionately lessened up to points 90° away, where there would be no lessening whatever of the gravitational forces. The result, therefore, would be to relatively weaken or nullify the gravitational forces along the direction of maximum attraction, through the centers of the two bodies, and to relatively strengthen the gravitational forces at right angles to this direction, thereby causing the attracted body to bulge outwardly toward the attracting body and also directly away from it, just as if the body was squeezed at right angles. Such an effect is illustrated by the ocean tides upon the Earth, where watery bulges are produced simultaneously on diametrically opposite areas of the Earth's surface,—one nearest the tide-producing body, whether the Moon or the Sun, and the other furthest away from it. The height of tidal bulges or prominences and their relative size on the near and far sides depends on the relative masses of the attracted and the attracting bodies, and on their relative proximity. Thus the lunar ocean tides on the Earth are weak, amounting to only a few feet, because of the small mass of the Moon and its considerable distance away; while the ratio of 30 to 31 in the distances of the near and far sides of the Earth from the Moon causes the lunar ocean tides on the two sides to be nearly equal, with a difference of about 5% in favor of the near side. The fact that the arms of most of the spiral galaxies are of very considerable length, as compared with the size of the hub, and that they are usually approximately equal in length, suggests that the attracting body, which produced them, must have been vastly larger, and also must have been at a considerable distance when the maximum effect was produced. This situation is best explained by the assumption that the arms were created, as tidal prominences, by the attraction of the residual portion of the Primordial Mass, at the time when the fragment, which ultimately developed into a spiral galaxy, departed from it, but that this fragment must have departed at a sufficiently high speed that the inertia of the constituents of the fragment and their resistance to deformation were not overcome and the formation of the tidal prominences attained its maximum development, until a considerable separation had taken place. The rotation of the fragment would explain the curved shape of the arms, and this effect would be enhanced if the vicinity of the fragment contained considerable lesser debris, which might obstruct and retard the rotation of the arms as compared with that of the hub. Tidal prominences would also be produced in non-rotating fragments, but they would eventually escape altogether or else fall back into the body of the fragment, depending on whether or not their speed of outward movement exceeded the retarding effect of the attraction of the body.

The development of stars, which constitutes the final phase in the formation of galaxies, appears to be a somewhat different process than the previous stages, in which original fragments of the Primordial Mass are assumed to have progressively subdivided into fragments of smaller and smaller size, until eventually pieces sufficiently small enough to possess relative stability and to resist further subdivision were produced. These pieces, like the Primordial Mass itself, are assumed to be composed of atoms of extraordinary weight and complexity, such as appear to constitute the star known as the Companion of Sirius, which has a specific gravity of 61,000, thus far transcending anything known on the Earth. These atoms, while stable within the Primordial Mass, under the tremendous pressure there existing, would be unstable when removed from that environment, and thereupon would begin to disintegrate into atoms of lighter weight and simpler structure, in the same manner that relatively heavy atoms, such as uranium and thorium, do in the Earth's crust. The disintegration of unstable atoms in the Earth's crust progresses simultaneously throughout all such atoms constituting a mineral in the Earth's crust, regardless of its size,—which, however, is always relatively small; but in the fragments of the Primordial Mass of star size,—24,800 miles diameter, in the case of the Sun, if possessing a specific gravity of 60,000,—there is reason to believe that the influence of the change of environment, resulting in reduction of the surrounding pressure, does not penetrate equally throughout the entire mass of the star, but is confined wholly or chiefly to its periphery, so that atomic disintegration is active only or principally on the surface and works inward only as fast as the surface atoms disintegrate and their products escape. In such a case the disintegration would be expected to progress inwardly at a linear speed, which would either remain fairly constant, or, more probably, would diminish somewhat with decrease of diameter of the mass; while the rate of disintegration would vary with the surface of the shrinking mass, or the square of its diameter, according to a curve (Figure 2 - 3) which would somewhat resemble the decay curve of unstable terrestrial atoms (Chapter I, Figure 1 - 5), but would, instead, have a finite termination.

It is assumed, therefore, that such a fragment of the Primordial Mass of star size would commence to disintegrate, wholly or chiefly on its periphery, with the evolution of light and heat; that the temperature so developed on its surface would probably attain several hundred thousand degrees Centigrade; that the end products of such disintegration would be atoms of simple composition and low weight, such as those now constituting the body of the Earth; that these atoms, at the temperature at which they were formed, would be gaseous and would surround the shrinking fragment of the Primor-

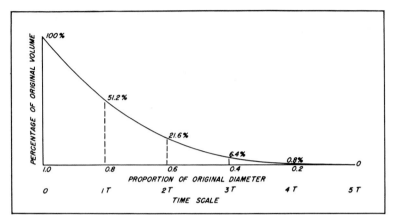

FIGURE 2 - 3

Decay curve of a star nucleus.

dial Mass like an atmosphere; and that there would thus be formed a
hot, luminous star, which would have at its center a nucleus of heavy,
complex atoms, intensely radioactive on its periphery, representing
the residue of the original fragment of the Primordial Mass, surrounded by an incandescent atmosphere of low density, composed of
simple atoms in gaseous form. The boundary between the nucleus
and the atmosphere, however, would not be sharp, because the disintegration of the atoms constituting the periphery of the nucleus
would take place in stages, probably extending over a considerable
period of time, so that the nucleus would be surounded by a zone of
intermediate disintegration products, lying between it and the atmosphere. Concurrently with the progressive radioactive disintegration
of the nucleus on its periphery, which would cause a constant transfer of mass from the nucleus to the atmosphere and thereby increase
the weight of the latter, the amount of heat supplied by the nucleus
to the atmosphere would progressively diminish, due to the decreasing surface area of the nucleus. This would progressively reduce
the average temperature of the atmosphere, which thereupon would
impart less kinetic energy to the molecules of gas composing it,
causing a reduction of the volume of the atmosphere despite its
increasing weight, thereby increasing its density. The reduction in
the average temperature of the atmosphere would be manifested by
a progressive drop in its surface temperature, which, after the star's
development was well under way, would cause the star gradually
to change in hue, from an original blue color, to white, to pale yellow,

to yellow and to red, in all of which stages, however, it would continue to be a hot, gaseous body of low average density, enclosing a small, high density, liquid or solid radioactive nucleus at its center. Eventually, however, the nucleus would become so small that the heat emitted by it would be insufficient to keep all of its disintegration products, constituting its atmosphere, in a gaseous condition; and thereupon there would be a partial condensation of the atmosphere into liquid and solid form, creating a spherical central rock body or lithosphere, surrounded concentrically by a hydrosphere or ocean of water, and that in turn by an atmosphere of uncondensed gases, forming a dark, non-luminous star, somewhat resembling the Earth in general character. The final stage of star development would commence when the nucleus had entirely disintegrated and disappeared, whereupon the star would consist of a central solid lithosphere, surrounded by a frozen ocean, but lacking an atmosphere, because at the temperature of space, to which it would be reduced, the atmospheric gases would be condensed to solid form.

For purposes of illustration, the progressive development of a star, according to the preceding outline, may be arbitrarily divided into eight stages, as shown in Figure 2 - 4, in which the dimensions shown would be those of the Sun.

Stage I.   Gradual commencement of the peripheral disintegration of a star-sized fragment of the Primordial Mass, forming a high density dwarf white star, with an approximate surface temperature of 12,000° K. and an assumed density of about 60,000 times that of water, consisting chiefly of nucleus, surrounded by a thin gaseous atmosphere.

Stage II.   Peripheral disintegration of the nucleus fully under way, with maximum evolution of heat, forming a thick atmosphere of disintegration products surrounding the nucleus, thus creating a main sequence blue star, with an approximate surface temperature of about 15,000° K. (although it may range much higher), and a density of only a fraction of that of water.

Stage III.   Shrinkage of the nucleus due to peripheral disintegration, accompanied by decrease in its surface area and consequent reduced evolution of heat, resulting in an increase in the weight of the surrounding gaseous atmosphere, but a decrease in its average temperature and its volume; thus creating a main sequence white star, with an approximate surface temperature of about 12,000° K. and a density somewhat higher than that of Stage II but still less than that of water.

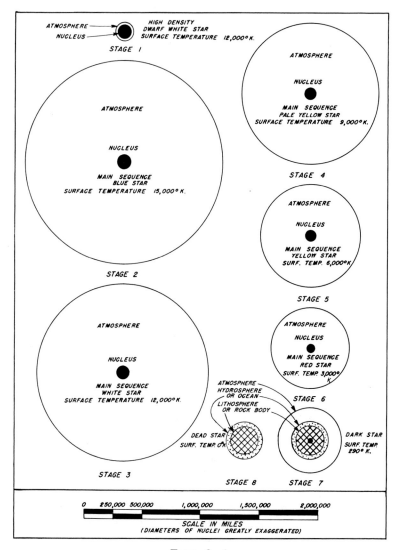

FIGURE 2 - 4

Illustrating diagrammatically the development of a star, with the Sun as an example. The sizes of the nuclei are greatly exaggerated.

Stage IV. Further shrinkage of the nucleus due to peripheral disintegration, accompanied by decrease in surface area and consequent reduced evolution of heat, resulting in a further decrease in average temperature and in the volume of its atmosphere; thus creating a main sequence pale yellow star, with an approximate surface temperature of about 9,000° K., and a density somewhat higher than that of Stage III, approaching that of water.

Stage V. Further shrinkage of the nucleus and consequent reduced evolution of heat, resulting in a further decrease in its average temperature and in the volume of its atmosphere; thus creating a main sequence yellow star, with an approximate surface temperature of about 6,000° K., and a density somewhat higher than that of Stage IV and a little greater than that of water. Example: the Sun.

Stage VI. Further shrinkage of the nucleus and consequent reduced evolution of heat, resulting in a further decrease in the average temperature and in the volume of its atmosphere; thus creating a main sequence red star, with an approximate surface temperature of about 3,000° K., and a density higher than that of Stage V and somewhat greater than that of water.

Stage VII. Further shrinkage of the nucleus and consequent reduced evolution of heat to the point where it is no longer sufficient to keep the atmosphere completely in a gaseous state, resulting in the condensation of the heavier molecules into liquids and solids and their gravitative separation from the remainder of the atmosphere and accumulation at depth; thus creating a dark, non-luminous star, consisting of a small, central nucleus, enclosed in a spherical, partly liquid, partly solid rock body (the lithosphere), surrounded concentrically by a body of water (the hydrosphere or ocean), and that in turn surrounded concentrically by an atmosphere of uncondensed gases. The surface temperature of the ocean would be approximately 290° K. but the temperature of the outer part of the atmosphere would be much lower; while the average density of the star would be perhaps twice that of water.

Stage VIII. Disappearance of the nucleus, due to completion of its disintegration, thus eliminating the source of internal heat; resulting in a "dead" star, consisting of a spherical solid central lithosphere, surrounded by a frozen ocean, but lacking an atmosphere, because at the temperature of absolute zero, to which the star would be reduced, the atmospheric gases would be condensed to solid form. The average density of the star would be several times that of water.

All intermediate stages between those described would occur, of course, and many variations, as to size, color, surface temperature and density, from the type stars described, are to be seen in the sky.

The fact that stars in all different stages of development exist in the heavens today is to be explained, partly by the fact that the formation of stars from fragments of the explosive disruption of the Primordial Mass is further advanced in some portions of a galaxy, where subdivision of the fragments down to star size has proceeded faster than in other portions, and partly by the fact that, the rate of disintegration of individual star nuclei being a function of their diameters, the small stars would tend to age more rapidly than the larger stars.

The most significant evidence in support of the validity of the hypothesis of star development previously advanced is furnished by the double or binary star Sirius, which, as described on page 25, consists of two members: a large, main sequence white star, known as Sirius A, which has a surface temperature of about 11,000° K., a density of 0.88 times that of water, a diameter about half as large again as the Sun, and a weight of about two and a half times as much; and a dwarf white star, known as Sirius B, with a surface temperature of about 8,000° K., a density of 61,000 times that of water, a diameter of only about 1/60th that of Sirius A, but a mass of about one third as much. Figure 2 - 5 provides a comparison between the

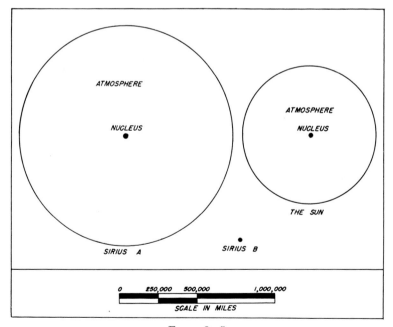

FIGURE 2 - 5

Illustrating diagrammatically the comparison between the stars, Sirius A, Sirius B and the Sun, as to size and constitution.

sizes of Sirius A, Sirius B and the Sun. Despite the seeming tremendous difference in character between Sirius A and Sirius B, there is reason to believe that they originally constituted a single star, which became divided into two parts in the following manner. A liquid mass or a plastic solid mass, acting like a fluid, if rotating with sufficient rapidity, will first form a flattened sphere or oblate spheroid; then the equator will lose its circular shape and become elliptical, forming an ellipsoid; then the longest diameter will elongate still further until a cigar-shaped figure is formed, with a length nearly three times its shortest diameter; and then a furrow will form on one side of the center and will deepen until it cuts the

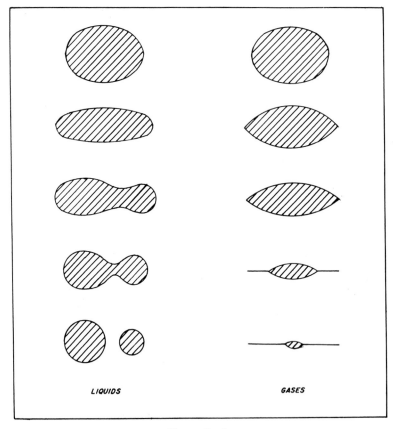

LIQUIDS   GASES

FIGURE 2 - 6

Illustrating diagrammatically the fission of a rapidly rotating liquid body and dispersal of a rapidly rotating gaseous body. ("*The Universe Around Us,*" by Sir James Jeans, p. 214. Copyright, 1931, The Cambridge University Press, New York, N. Y.)

body into two masses of unequal size. A binary pair of stars, formed in this way, revolves about the common center of gravity, while the large body tides raised in each by the attraction of the other tend to drive them further and further apart. A mass of gas, subject to the same excessive rate of rotation, would not divide into two parts in similar fashion, but the molecules of gas would tend to be thrown off individually from its equator by centrifugal force, so that it would gradually waste away.

Sirius B, with its tremendous density, must be chiefly either in solid or liquid form, and the corresponding liquid or solid part of Sirius A must exist deep within its atmosphere, forming the nucleus of the star. The only difference between the two stars, therefore, would be that, since the time of their separation from each other to form a binary star, Sirius A has developed a very large atmosphere surrounding its nucleus, so that the average density of the entire star has become less than that of water, while the development of the atmosphere of Sirius B, which must be very thin, has lagged far behind, so that its nucleus constitutes nearly all of the mass of the star. Three possible explanations of this circumstance may be set forth. One is that the original single star Sirius, prior to its fission into the pair of stars Sirius A and Sirius B, had developed a large atmosphere, most of which accompanied the larger and weightier of the two stars at the time of their separation. Another is that, for some reason, the peripheral atomic disintegration of a large star mass may start sooner than that of a small star mass, so that a large star mass may commence to develop a gaseous atmosphere earlier than a small star mass. A third is that the disintegration of the surface of a fragment of the Primordial Mass may not commence spontaneously upon its separation and relief from surrounding pressure, but may require some sort of trigger action to start it, and this trigger action may vary in different stars as to the time when it takes place. The latter, if true, would help to explain why different stars are in different stages of development.

The high density of Sirius B, which has been so well established by astronomical observations as to leave no room for doubt, and which is parallelled by similar high densities in other dwarf stars, may be explained in two ways. Under sufficiently high temperatures, the orbital electrons of atoms may be stripped off in star interiors, and the bare nuclei, under great pressure, may be compressed into masses of high density. However, it requires temperatures of the order of from $15,000,000°$ K. to $25,000,000°$ K. to accomplish the stripping of atomic nuclei in this fashion, and such extremely high temperatures could not exist in the interior of Sirius B, which has a radius of only about 11,700 miles, without being reflected in a surface temperature of far higher than that of 8,000° K., which Sirius B actually possesses.

The only alternative explanation is that Sirius B is composed of atoms of far greater weight than any existing on the surface of the Earth. Consideration of the peculiarities of stellar development from the original Primordial Mass suggests that such atoms, which hereafter will be referred to as Q-atoms, have the following characteristics. A Q-atom possesses great weight and structural complexity. It probably is stable only under enormous pressure, and becomes potentially unstable when such pressure starts to decrease, although it may not then spontaneously start to decay, but may require some outside stimulus. Once begun, however, decay may progress automatically without further incentive, at a more or less constant rate, both by the process of disintegration into electrons, protons, neutrons, helium nuclei and radiation, and by the process of fission into two or more smaller atoms, with accompanying radiation. Consequently a mass of Q-atoms decays, not throughout at the same rate, but wholly or principally on its periphery, where decrease in pressure is most manifest, and the decay works inward at a radial speed, which probably diminishes gradually, as the products of disintegration accumulate about the mass, and exert increasing pressure upon it.

A Q-atom is probably constituted in one of the three following possible ways: (1) It may be an extrapolation of heavy terrestrial atoms like uranium and be similarly composed of electrons, protons and neutrons, but of far great complexity, with a formula possibly somewhat like $_{100000}Q^{600000}$. On the Earth such an atom would probably be so unstable that it would disintegrate almost instantaneously, with explosive violence; and it seems rather unlikely that even in stellar interiors it would have the properties that Q-atoms seem to possess. (2) It may have a somewhat similar structure to the preceding, but be composed wholly of neutrons, forming a polyneutron complex, with a formula possibly somewhat like $_0Q^{600000}$. The fact that on the Earth a free neutron disintegrates spontaneously into an electron, a proton and a neutrino, with a half-life of from ten to twenty minutes, while a neutron in the nucleus of one of the stable isotopes may remain in that condition indefinitely, suggests that in a fragment of the Primordial Mass, composed of Q-atoms, which were polyneutron complexes, the external atoms might tend to disintegrate spontaneously, while those in its interior, still subject to high pressure, might remain stable until exposed to outside influences in their turn. (3) It may be, like the neutron, a primary particle,—primary in the sense that, while composite in structure, its constituents are so tightly bound together that they behave quite differently from the looser aggregations that form ordinary atoms. In this respect, it may be somewhat similar to one of the bricks, of which a house is built, and which, although composed of clay, sand and gravel, into which it may be resolved again under stress, is a unit of construction. Such a particle might be designated a super-neutron.

It appears probable, therefore, that a Q-atom is either a polyneutron complex or a primary particle such as has been designated a super-neutron, and that, in either case, having been formed or having existed under terrific, long-continued pressure in the interior of the Primordial Mass, it possesses or has acquired properties quite different from those of terrestrial atoms, and that, under reduction of pressure, it tends to disintegrate into lighter and simpler atoms.

Variable stars and novae furnish evidence supporting the probable existence of intensely radioactive, high density nuclei at the centers of stars, where heat, light and other forms of radiation appear to be generated in great abundance. The escape of such radiation through the gaseous envelope, which constitutes the atmosphere of a star, is primarily accomplished by actual migration of such radiation outwardly through this atmosphere, aided by convection currents in it, but if this method is not sufficient for the purpose, the radiation will adopt supplementary and more violent methods of escape. As will be shown in the following chapter, the radiation of the Sun intermittently creates and utilizes solar cyclones in its atmosphere for this purpose, and the same or a similar emergency process seems to take place, to a much greater extent, in the larger and hotter stars, which constitute the Cepheid variables. Surplus radiation appears to accumulate deep within the body of such a star, around the radiation generating nucleus at its center, until sufficient pressure has been built up to lift the entire superincumbent atmosphere, through which it then bursts in some manner or other,—this action taking place at regular intervals, forming a cycle. Other types of variable stars are probably due to the same cause, acting with different intensities; while in a nova, the accumulation of radiation pressure, which similarly brings about the catastrophic disruption and distension of its atmosphere, may be caused by some exceptional event, such as the fission of its nucleus into two parts, to eventually form a binary star.

The Earth's atmosphere is being constantly bombarded, at all hours of the day and night, and from all directions, by what are called cosmic rays. These consist of electrified particles, of which about 80% are protons or nuclei of the hydrogen atom, while most of the remainder are alpha particles or nuclei of the helium atom. The balance, amounting to less than 1%, consist of nuclei of atoms of the heavier elements, usually in diminishing amount proportional to the increase in atomic weight. No nuclei of elements heavier than iron have been observed. The relative abundance of elements in cosmic rays is quite similar to the abundance observed spectroscopically in stellar atmospheres. On the average, about six of such particles per minute impinge upon each square inch of the outer area of the Earth's atmosphere, and the amount of energy of this nature received by the Earth within a given time is approximately equal to that brought in by starlight.

Cosmic rays are notable for the energies they possess, which is greater than that of any other known form of radiation. The energy of a single cosmic ray of the most powerful type is a billion times that released from a single uranium atom in the explosion of an atomic bomb. Cosmic rays arrive with a wide range of velocities, sometimes approaching the speed of light, and their energies correspondingly vary widely. Some are greater than a billion electron volts per particle; others of more than ten billion electron volts have been measured directly; while energies as large as 10^{16} electron volts are required to explain some of the secondary phenomena, that have been observed.

Cosmic rays approaching the Earth are deflected, in inverse proportion to the energy they possess, by the Earth's magnetic field, which extends for thousands of miles out into space, far beyond the limits of its atmosphere. The deflecting power is smallest at the Earth's north and south geomagnetic poles, within the Arctic and Antarctic Circles, and greatest at the geomagnetic equator, halfway between. Hence only the strongest cosmic rays penetrate in the Earth's equatorial regions, while weaker rays penetrate in increasing

FOOTNOTE: An electron volt is the energy, which a charge equal to 1.6×10^{-19} coulomb obtains in falling through a potential difference of one volt. One electron volt equals 1.6×10^{-12} erg.

abundance in higher latitudes. Cosmic rays obviously must originate somewhere outside of the Earth. Some of the weaker rays may have been born in the Sun, as such rays do not possess sufficient energy to have enabled them to travel from more distant sources; and this conclusion is strengthened by the fact that these weaker rays seem to increase in number during solar electro-magnetic disturbances, indicated by solar prominences. The more energetic rays probably originate beyond the Sun, from other and hotter members of the Milky Way galaxy. It seems possible that cosmic rays may represent some of the decomposition products of Q-atoms, constituting the nuclei of the stars, and that such decomposition products, which have had to struggle upwards through thick stellar atmospheres, such as that of the Sun, have lost so much energy by the time they emerge, that they become cosmic rays of weaker type; those, which have penetrated through the comparatively thin atmospheres of white dwarf stars of high density, may retain more of their original energies, and thus possess higher velocities; those, which have escaped from deeper levels of variable stars, during periods of atmospheric rupture, may have still greater energies; while those expelled during the catastrophic disruption of the atmospheres of novae and super-novae, could well be of intensity equal to the highest known.

The Devolutionary Hypothesis, which has now been discussed at considerable length, is consistent with the Second Law of Thermodynamics and with the Law of the Degradation of Energy, while it explains more or less competently all of the more important phenomena of the Universe, with the exception of the most momentous problem of all, which so far has not been touched upon: what has been the mode of origin of the Primordial Mass, through whose explosive disruption the Universe is assumed to have developed. Until recent centuries, human vanity has tended to disparage the relative importance of distant celestial objects, and it has been only in the last half of the second millenium A. D., that mankind's cosmic horizon has expanded in this respect. Up to 1522, when the rotundity of the Earth was first directly proved and its actual size indicated by its initial circumnavigation by the Portuguese mariner Magellan, the Earth, of which the known portion was limited to the southern parts of Europe and Asia and the northern part of Africa, was generally considered to be flat and elliptical in outline, and to be covered by a star-studded, dome-shaped sky. Some twenty years afterwards the astronomer Copernicus correctly described the true nature of the Solar System, and showed that the Earth, which had formerly been supposed to constitute its center and to be its most important member, actually formed only a small part of it. About two hundred and fifty years later the astronomer Sir William Herschel described the nature of the Milky Way galaxy, and called attention to the fact that the Solar System is a relatively unimportant member of it; while, within the last fifty years, living astronomers have shown the Milky Way galaxy to be merely an undistinguished unit among myriads of similar galaxies, constituting the so-called Universe. Although the limits of the Universe have not been reached by the largest telescope, they are doubtless finite like those of its constituent galaxies.

Four hundred and fifty years ago, therefore, the limits of the Earth formed the cosmic frontier of mankind; but later investigation proved that the Earth was not self-sufficient, self-created nor self-perpetuating, but was simply a small cog in a much larger and more complex organization, the Solar System, which mankind's cosmic frontier was then extended to embrace. In its turn, the Solar System was found not to be self-sufficient, self-created nor self-perpetuating, but only an insignificant constituent of a vaster organization, the Milky Way galaxy, and mankind's cosmic frontier was expanded accordingly. So also the Milky Way galaxy proved not to be self-sufficient, self-created nor self-perpetuating, but only a single unit among the myriad galaxies constituting the Universe. Is there any reason to believe that the Universe is the last and final frontier, the ultimate goal? None whatever! The Second Law of Thermodynamics and the Law of the Degradation of Energy have clearly demonstrated that the Universe is no more self-sufficient, self-created nor self-perpetuating than its predecessors. So in its turn it may be a part, and possibly only a very minute and insignificant part of a vastly larger and more complex organization,—a sort of Super-Universe. Such being the case, the highly organized nature of the Primordial Mass need occasion no question. The secret of its origin, therefore, is assumed to lie within the Super-Universe, where it may well be only one among countless other Primordial Masses, which exist or once existed there,—all or many of which may also have developed into Universes; but in the complete absence of evidence, this is purely speculation at the present time. The Devolutionary Hypothesis, therefore, makes no pretense of attempting to solve the riddle of the Universe, by which is meant the determination of its ultimate origin. It merely points out that the Universe may not be and probably is not the last stage in cosmic development, and awaits future astronomical discoveries before proceeding further.

CHAPTER THREE

The Constitution of the Solar System

The Solar System consists of a single hot, luminous star,—the Sun; its attendant progeny, the planets; and their attendant progeny, the satellites. The planets and satellites are entirely unlike the Sun in physical constitution at the present time, however closely they may once have resembled it; for they are all non-luminous, relatively cold, solid, or partly liquid, partly solid bodies, with or without enveloping atmospheres, and they shine only by reflected light. The planets revolve in elliptical orbits around the Sun, and the satellites revolve in elliptical orbits around those planets, which they attend. More than fifteen hundred planets are known at the present time, but it is customary to confine the term to the nine largest, named in order of increasing distance from the Sun: Mercury, Venus, Earth, Mars, Jupiter, Saturn, Uranus, Neptune and Pluto, and to designate the remainder, all of which are very small, and which constitute a numerous group, lying in general between the orbits of Mars and Jupiter, under the collective name of the Asteroids. Six of the planets are known to have satellites, totalling 28 in number,—the Earth having one (the Moon), Mars two, Jupiter eleven, Saturn nine, Uranus four and Neptune one. Plate XVI shows the Sun and the planets drawn to scale, with the planets arranged in the order of their distances from the Sun,—Mercury being the closest and Pluto the furthest; while Figure 3 - 1 shows the relative distances of the planets from the Sun.

The principal elements of the Solar System are shown in Table II.

About one hundred and fifty years ago, the French astronomer LaPlace called attention to the following harmonious features of the Solar System, as then known,—the planets Neptune and Pluto, together with fourteen of the satellites, not yet having been discovered.

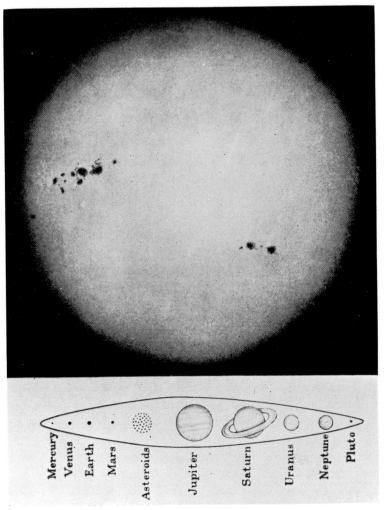

PLATE XVI

The Sun and planets drawn to scale, with the planets arranged in order from the Sun. Only the sizes, not the distances, are drawn to scale. If the distances were to scale, the Earth would be 11 yards and Pluto a quarter of a mile away from the Sun. (*"The Stars In Their Courses,"* by Sir James Jeans, p. 46. Copyright, 1931, The Cambridge University Press, New York, N. Y.)

1. All the planets revolved around the Sun in planes which nearly coincided with the plane of the Sun's rotation.

2. All the planets revolved around the Sun in the same direction (counter-clockwise), which was the same as the direction of the Sun's rotation on its axis.

3. All the planets rotated on their axes in the same direction (counter-clockwise), which was the same as the direction of the Sun's rotation on its axis.

4. Each of the satellites revolved around its respective planet in a plane, which nearly coincided with the plane of the planet's revolution, and in the same direction that the planet revolved around the Sun, while it rotated on its axis in the same direction that the planet rotated.

5. Each satellite revolved around its planet in a longer period of time than the period of the planet's rotation.

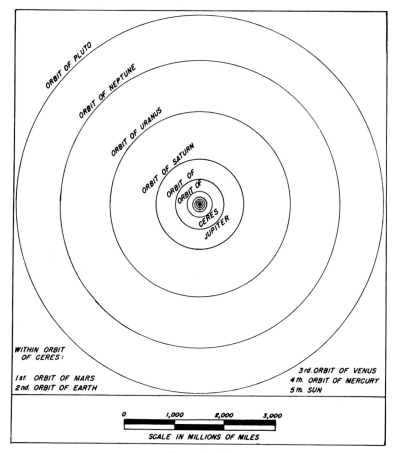

FIGURE 3 - 1

Illustrating diagrammatically the spacing of the planetary orbits of the Solar System, which, for the sake of simplicity, are shown as circles, instead of ellipses as they really are.

TABLE II.

	Equatorial Diameter Miles	Earth: 1	Volume Earth: 1	Mass Earth: 1	Mean Density Earth: 1	Water: 1
Sun	865,400	109.3	1,306,000	333,420	0.255	1.41
Moon	2,160	0.272	0.0203	0.0123	0.604	3.33
Mercury	3,000	0.378	0.055	0.037	0.68	3.73
Venus	7,600	0.959	0.876	0.826	0.94	5.21
Earth	7,927	1.000	1.000	1.000	1.000	5.52
Mars	4,200	0.530	0.151	0.108	0.71	3.95
Ceres	485	0.060	0.0002	0.00012	0.60	3.33 (?)
Jupiter	88,770	10.97	1318.	318.4	0.24	1.33
Saturn	74,200	9.03	736.	95.3	0.13	0.72
Uranus	32,400	4.00	64.	14.6	0.23	1.26
Neptune	30,900	3.90	60.	17.3	0.29	1.60
Pluto	7,900 (?)	1.0 (?)	1.0 (?)	0.93	1.0 (?)	5.0 (?)

	Axial Rotation	Inclination of Equator to Orbit	Oblate-ness	Albedo	Vel. of Escape Km/Sec.
Sun	24.65 d. (equatorial)	7°10.5′	0.0000		618.
Moon	27d 7h 43m 11.5s	6°40.7′	0.0004	0.07	2.4
Mercury	88d	Near zero	0.00	0.07	3.8
Venus	(?)	(?)	0.00	0.59	10.2
Earth	23h 56m 4.1s	23°27′	1/297	0.29	11.2
Mars	24h 37m 22.6s	25°12′	1/192	0.15	5.0
Ceres				0.06	0.5 (?)
Jupiter	9h 50.5m to 9h 56m	3°7′	1/15.4	0.44	60.
Saturn	10h 14m to 10h 38m	26°43′	1/9.5	0.42	36.
Uranus	10.7h	98.0°	1/14	0.45	21.
Neptune	15.8h	29°	1/45	0.52	23.
Pluto	Unknown			0.03 (?)	11.

	Semi-Major Axis of Orbit Earth: 1	Mean Distance From Sun Millions of Miles	Sidereal Period of Revolution in Years	Black Sphere Temperature	Mean Orbital Velocity (Km/sec.)	Inclination to Ecliptic	Eccentricity of Orbit
Mercury	0.387099	36.0	0.2408	172° C.	47.90	7°00′13.4″	0.20562
Venus	0.723331	67.3	0.6512	53° C.	35.05	3°23′38.7″	0.00680
Earth	1.000000	93.0	1.0000	4° C.	29.80	0	0.01673
Mars	1.523688	141.7	1.881	— 49° C.	24.14	1°51′ 0.1″	0.09335
Ceres	2.767303	257.4	4.6035		17.91	10°36′56″	0.07653
Jupiter	5.202803	483.9	11.862	—152° C.	13.06	1°18′22.3″	0.04841
Saturn	9.538843	887.1	29.458	—183° C.	9.65	2°29′25.9″	0.05573
Uranus	19.190978	1785.0	84.015	—210° C.	6.80	0°46′22.6″	0.04717
Neptune	30.070672	2797.0	164.788	—221° C.	5.43	1°46′29.8″	0.00856
Pluto	39.45743	3670.0	247.697	—229° C.	4.74	17° 8′35.1″	0.24852

TABLE II.—Continued

Notes:

The planet Ceres is the largest of the Asteroids.

The albedo of a planet or satellite is the proportion of the total amount of sunlight falling upon it, that is reflected from its surface.

The oblateness of a planet or satellite is the proportion of the shortening of its polar diameter as compared with its equatorial diameter.

The black sphere temperature of a planet or satellite is the temperature it would have if, as a rapidly rotating black sphere, it was a perfect absorber, conductor and radiator of the Sun's heat falling upon it.

The ecliptic is the plane of the Earth's orbit around the Sun.

The velocity of escape is the lowest velocity, at which a molecule of gas in the planet's atmosphere can escape from the attraction of the planet at its surface.

---

6. All the orbits of the planets were concentric in a general way,—that is, the orbit of one did not cross the orbit of any other.

7. The planets were spaced outwardly from the Sun according to a certain degree of symmetry.

To explain this harmony in the arrangement of the Solar System, LaPlace proposed what has since been called the Nebular Hypothesis. According to this hypothesis, the Solar System is supposed to have originated as a hot, gaseous nebula of discoidal shape, which extended beyond the outermost planetary orbit. Because of the mutual attraction of its constituents, the nebula slowly contracted towards its center, acquiring in this process a rotary motion, which accelerated as the shrinkage of the nebula progressed, as required to preserve its angular momentum. As the rate of rotation increased, so did the centrifugal force at its periphery, until eventually it exceeded the force of gravity, whereupon a ring of nebulous matter there became detached, which gradually collected into a spherical mass that, because of its inherited motion, revolved about the parent nebula in its equatorial plane, and eventually formed a planet. As the nebula contracted further, successive equatorial rings were detached, each of which in turn collected together and condensed to form a planet, while eventually the residual mass of the nebula, after the secession of seven such rings to form the planets then known, condensed to form the Sun, the cooling of which is still in progress. Those of the planets, now accompanied by satellites, are

---

FOOTNOTE: Most of the statistics in Table II are quoted from *"Astronomy,"* by H. N. Russell, R. S. Dugan and J. Q. Stewart. Copyright, 1945, by Ginn and Company, Boston, Mass.

supposed to have detached one or more equatorial rings, in the course of their condensations, and these eventually became the satellites. According to this hypothesis, the members of the Solar System would vary widely in age,—Uranus, the outermost planet then known, being the oldest, and Mercury, the innermost planet, the youngest, while the Sun would be younger still. The Nebular Hypothesis is engaging because of its apparent simplicity, and because of its seeming harmony with the features of the Solar System; while the rings, which encircle the planet Saturn in its equatorial plane close to its surface, were then supposed to be gaseous and to provide a perfect example of a satellite in course of formation, thus supplying proof of the validity of the hypothesis. Until the present century, therefore, the Nebular Hypothesis was generally accepted; but by that time a number of inconsistencies had developed.

1. The rings of the planet Saturn, instead of being gaseous, have been found to consist of a large number of solid bodies, probably of meteoric dimensions, presumably formed by the disruption of a former satellite, due to the attraction of the planet.

2. Five or more of the satellites revolve in a retrograde direction and in planes at high angles to the equatorial planes of the planets they attend.

3. The innermost of the two moons of the planet Mars revolves about it in a shorter period of time than that of the rotation of the planet itself on its axis.

4. According to the Nebular Hypothesis, the planets should revolve around the Sun in approximately the plane of the Sun's equator, but the weighted average of the orbital planes of the entire planetary group is inclined about 7° to the Sun's equatorial plane.

5. The orbits of some of the Asteroids cross the orbits of Jupiter and Mars.

6. According to stellar dynamics, a rotating disk, like the assumed parent nebula, would not disengage rings at its periphery, when the centrifugal force exceeded that of gravity, but the molecules of gas would tend to fly off individually, like particles of mud from a cart-wheel.

7. If the Solar System had been formed in the manner described, the Sun, having 744/745ths of the total mass of the Solar System, should have 744/745ths of its angular momentum, as the latter would neither be increased nor decreased by the assumed method of formation. But, as a matter of fact, the Sun possesses less than

2% of the total angular momentum of the Solar System, while the planets and their satellites, although containing only 1/745th of the total mass of the system, possess over 98% of its angular momentum.

On account of these discrepancies, and particularly the last, which fatally affects its validity, the Nebular Hypothesis was supplanted in scientific esteem, early in this century, by the Tidal Theory of the origin of the Solar System, which was first proposed by T. C. Chamberlin and F. R. Moulton, and has since been advocated in somewhat modified form by Sir J. H. Jeans, Harold Jeffreys and others. According to the Chamberlin-Moulton hypothesis, the Sun originally existed as a solitary star, a member of the Milky Way galaxy, and it was hot and gaseous throughout, much like its supposed present condition. In this situation a stranger star, presumably also a member of the Milky Way galaxy, but with different speed and somewhat different direction of movement, approached the Sun or was overtaken by it. This other star is presumed to have been of large dimensions, equal to that of the Sun or larger. The two stars are assumed to have passed each other very closely, with the result that their mutual attraction raised huge tidal bulges on the surface of each, in the direction of the other, and probably also, to a lesser extent, in the opposite direction, according to the theory of tidal action. The tidal bulge on the Sun in the direction of the stranger star is supposed to have been stretched out so far, and to have been affected as to its direction by the relative motion of the stranger, so as to form a curved arm or filament, like one of the arms of a spiral galaxy, which, after the departure of the stranger, did not fall back into the body of the Sun, but revolved around it, eventually condensing into a large number of small bodies (planetesimals), that subsequently collected to form the planets and their satellites. This theory satisfactorily accounts for the much larger angular momentum of the planets and satellites than that of the Sun, but it is subject to other objections, of which the two following are the most vital.

1. Since the material ejected from the Sun, to form the tidal arms, would be gaseous, at a very high temperature, which would cause its molecules to be travelling at terrific speed, it is probable that such molecules, when released from the attraction of the Sun, would disperse rapidly through space and never aggregate and condense into liquid and then solid masses to form the planets and their satellites.

2. The tide raising force is proportional to the mass of the attracting body and inversely proportional to the cube of the dis-

tance. Hence it seems highly improbable that the stranger star, approximately the size of the Sun or somewhat larger, could draw a tidal filament from the Sun out to a distance of 3,670,000,000 miles,—that of the planet Pluto,—or over 4,000 times the Sun's diameter, where the attraction of the stranger star would have been reduced to 1.56×10^{-13} of what it was, when passing the Sun one diameter distant.

Modified forms of the Tidal Theory have since been proposed, according to one of which there was actually a glancing collision between the Sun and the stranger star, while, according to another the Sun was originally a twin star, and the stranger star collided with and totally demolished the Sun's companion. In each case the material driven out into space by the impact of the two stars is supposed to have furnished the substance from which the planets and satellites were subsequently formed. These modifications of the Tidal Theory also have their difficulties, of which the two following are the chief ones.

1. Even more than in the original Tidal Theory, it is probable that the gaseous molecules, liberated from the stellar interiors by the collision, would disperse through space, instead of aggregating to form the planets and satellites, because, originating deeper within the bodies of the stars, they would be much hotter and hence have higher velocities.

2. The material driven out into space by the impact of the collision would tend to be sprayed out and widely scattered, and hence there would be even less opportunity, than when a tidal filament was formed, for it to collect into planets and satellites.

As a final criticism, the Tidal Theory of the formation of the Solar System is based on the Evolutionary Hypothesis as to the formation of the Sun by the aggregation of primitive matter originally widely dispersed through space, which, as previously explained, is inconsistent with the Second Law of Thermodynamics and the Law of the Degradation of Energy.

All the inconsistencies of the Evolutionary Hypothesis, as applied to the origin of the Solar System, can be remedied under the opposite Devolutionary Hypothesis. The Sun, being situated about two-thirds of the distance from the center of the Milky Way galaxy to its periphery, must be located in one of its two tidal arms, if, as believed, this galaxy is in spiral form, resembling the Andromeda galaxy. Acording to the Devolutionary Hypothesis, the Milky Way galaxy represents one of the original fragments of the Primordial Mass, which, at the time of its separation, developed two spiral tidal arms, through the attraction of the portion of the Primordial Mass remaining behind. These tidal arms consisted of separate sub-fragments, which were expelled from the original fragment, and they in turn were explosively disrupted into much smaller masses, which eventually developed into stars. The Sun was formed by the explosive disruption of such a sub-fragment located in one of the spiral arms of the Milky Way galaxy, about two thirds of the distance from the center of its hub to its tip. At the time of its separation, the Sun was subject to the attraction of the remainder of the sub-fragment, lying inwardly from it, and as a consequence of this attraction two tidal arms were drawn out from the body of the departing Sun; and as the outward speed of the Sun was large, these tidal arms did not reach their fullest extension until the Sun was distant several thousand times its diameter from the parent sub-fragment, thus permitting the formation of tidal arms of comparable length, some 4,000 times the Sun's diameter. The tidal arms con-sisted of separate small masses of the same material as that of which the body of the Sun was composed; and this material, consisting of a viscous liquid or a plastic solid capable of acting like a fluid, would have the tendency to adjust its shape with relative rapidity into masses of more or less spherical form, hereinafter referred to as "blobs." It will impose much less strain on the imagination to conceive of such blobs, each of planetary mass, already in a liquid or solid state, and spaced more or less regularly outwardly from the Sun, developing into a planetary system, than the formless masses of hot, incohesive, furiously active gases, which are assumed to have been the progenitors of the planets, according to the Evolutionary Hypothesis. Since the Sun was rotating, as it departed from the parent sub-fragment, the tidal arms tended to wrap around the body of the Sun, and thereby the planets, eventually formed from these spiral arms, acquired their orbital motion around the Sun. The mode of formation of the Solar System, consequently, was almost identical with the mode of formation of the Milky Way galaxy, of which it constituted a replica in miniature.

To follow the development of the Sun from its initial stage, as a star-sized subdivision of a larger sub-fragment of the Primordial Mass, it is necessary to consider its present condition, as a hot, yellow star. It is a spherical body, showing no signs of flattening at the poles. Its counter-clockwise rotation period varies according to latitude, being fastest at the equator, where the time of one revolution is 24.65 days, and slowest at the poles, where it is 34 days. There must, therefore, be an equatorial current of unknown but probably great depth, running eastwards with a velocity of 1230 miles an hour, which gradually diminishes towards the poles but so slowly as to cause little disturbance. The diameter is 865,400 miles, or 109.3 times that of the Earth. The visible body of the Sun is the top of the brilliantly luminous but opaque gaseous layer, known as the photosphere, which has a temperature of about 6,000° K., and below which vision cannot penetrate. Outside of the photosphere are two transparent layers,—the lowermost, with a thickness of 500 miles, and a probable temperature of about 5,000° K. being called the reversing layer; while outside of it is the chromosphere, some 8,000 to 9,000 miles thick, which has a temperature of about 4,000° K., and consists principally of hydrogen, helium and ionized calcium. Sixty-six of the 98 known terrestrial chemical elements have been identified in the Sun, most of them occurring in the reversing layer. The Sun's mass is 333,420 times that of the Earth, and its density is 1.41 times that of water, or a little more than a fourth of that of the Earth.

The Sun is not simply an originally hot body, which is passively cooling. Every second it expels from its surface about 4,641,000 tons of energy, in the form of heat, light and other radiation, with a violence which indicates that this energy is being actively generated somewhere within its body. Most of this energy struggles up through the mass of the Sun to its surface by means of radiation pressure; but the total amount of energy generated in the Sun is more than can be disposed of by this process, which has to be supplemented at intervals by the formation of sunspots. Sunspots, which intermittently form dark spots or blotches on the Sun's glowing face, ranging from 500 to 50,000 miles in diameter, are actually solar cyclones, consisting of vortical or swirling columns of hot gases, rising from somewhere in the interior of the Sun to its surface, similar in form to the vortex created by water draining from a sink, but in the opposite direction. Like terrestrial cyclones, these solar cyclones also have an advancing movement, averaging about 250 miles an hour, in addition to their swirling motion. It is probable that they are formed in somewhat similar fashion to some terrestrial cyclones. When the layer of air next to the Earth's surface becomes heated by the Sun faster than the heat can be radiated outwards through the atmosphere, a local atmospheric instability is then created, because this lowest layer of air is lighter than the atmos-

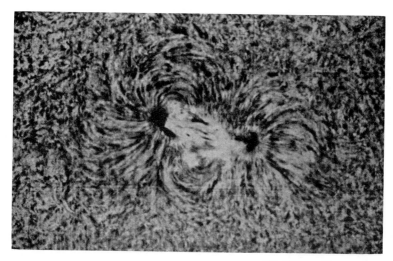

Mt. Wilson Observatory.

PLATE XVII

A pair of sunspots on the surface of the Sun, showing the effects of the disturbance caused by their vortical motion.

phere directly overlying it. This instability is relieved by the heated air of the lowest atmospheric layer forcing a passage through the overlying layer at some point, whereupon the air in the heated layer next to the Earth tends to rush from all sides towards this point of escape, up which it ascends violently with a twisting or vortical motion until it reaches an upper level, where it is in equilibrium with the surrounding atmosphere, and then tends to flow outwardly and eventually descend, as illustrated in the accompanying Figure 3 - 2.

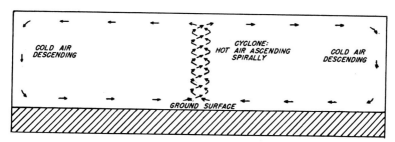

FIGURE 3 - 2

Illustrating diagrammatically the atmospheric circulation in the formation of some terrestrial cyclones, according to the so-called convection theory.

This circumstance suggests that solar cyclones or sunspots constitute the agency, whereby surplus interior solar heat, which is generated faster than it can be conveyed upwards through the Sun's atmosphere by means of radiation and convectional currents, is disposed of; and this conclusion seems to be supported by the fact that the total amount of radiation from the Sun appears to be about 2% greater than normal, during years when sunspots are most numerous. The fact that sunspots tend to attain their maxima in cycles of about eleven years on the average suggests that it is only after a sufficient period of heat accumulation within the body of the Sun that the disposal of excess heat by means of solar cyclones tends to occur.

The conventional view of the constitution of the Sun, based on the Evolutionary Hypothesis, is that it is completely gaseous from surface to center, in which case the pressure would exceed a billion atmospheres (14.7 x 10^9 pounds) at the center, if the Sun were of uniform density throughout, while it would be greater still if, as expected, the density of the center were greater than the average, amounting possibly to about 110 times that of water. The central temperature is estimated to be somewhere between 20,000,000° K. and 40,000,000° K., as would be necessary to impart sufficient velocity to the gaseous atoms there to sustain the superincumbent weight. The earliest theory as to the source of solar energy was proposed by Helmholtz, who pointed out that, as the Sun cooled, it must shrink, and as it shrank the energy of the fall of the material towards its center would be converted into heat; but as the life of the Sun, according to this hypothesis, would be only 25,000,000 years, which is far less than is indicated by other lines of evidence, this theory would be hardly an adequate explanation. It has been supplanted in scientific esteem by the hypothesis of Bethe, who has suggested that the Sun's energy is provided by the synthesis of hydrogen atoms into helium atoms within the body of the Sun, by means of isotopes of carbon, nitrogen and oxygen, acting as catalysts, according to the following chain of reactions:

$$Carbon^{12} + Hydrogen^1 \rightarrow Nitrogen^{13} + gamma\ ray$$
$$Nitrogen^{13} \rightarrow Carbon^{13} + positron$$
$$Carbon^{13} + Hydrogen^1 \rightarrow Nitrogen^{14} + gamma\ ray$$
$$Nitrogen^{14} + Hydrogen^1 \rightarrow Oxygen^{15} + gamma\ ray$$
$$Oxygen^{15} \rightarrow Nitrogen^{15} + positron$$
$$Nitrogen^{15} + Hydrogen^1 \rightarrow Carbon^{12} + Helium^4$$

The atomic weight of helium is less than the combined atomic weights of the four atoms of hydrogen, which, according to this formula, would be converted into one atom of helium; and thus, for every 400 grams of hydrogen thus transmuted, about 3 grams of radiation would be released. This is sufficient energy to maintain the Sun at its present temperature for some 35,000,000,000 years, if the Sun's atmosphere contains as much hydrogen as assumed. Each step in this process has been duplicated artificially in the laboratory, so that the method is theoretically possible; but a natural environment in the Sun, where such a reaction could take place, would require, at such locality, a temperature in excess of 25,000,000° K., under which the atoms would be completely denuded of their orbital electrons, and would be reduced to atomic nuclei and free electrons. This hypothesis is plausible, because of the known presence of hydrogen in apparently large volume in the Sun's atmosphere, but it is not supported by any corroborative evidence to show that it is actually taking place. The chief objection to it is that it is inconsistent with certain geological phenomena, to be later discussed, which must tie in somehow with the origin and development of the Solar System as a whole.

A Sun quite different in character from that assumed under the Evolutionary Hypothesis is indicated under the Devolutionary Hypothesis. As previously described, the Sun is supposed, under this latter hypothesis, to have originated as a relatively small subdivision of an explosively disintegrated sub-fragment of the Primordial Mass, situated in one of the spiral arms of the Milky Way galaxy. The matter composing this primeval Sun is believed to have been a viscous liquid or plastic solid of enormous density, assumed to be about 60,000 times that of water, similar to that of the star known as the Companion of Sirius, and to be composed of comparably heavy and complex atoms, for which the name Q-atoms has previously been suggested. In this condition, the original Sun, if it had the same total mass as at present, would have had, if spherical, a diameter of about 24,800 miles. The heavy and complex Q-atoms composing the primeval Sun, when removed from their original high pressure environment, are assumed to have become potentially unstable, and therefore subject to disintegration into lighter and simpler atoms,—particularly around the Sun's periphery, where relief from pressure would be most manifest, and therefore atomic instability most pronounced,—with the evolution of light, heat and other forms of radiation. Because of the heat evolved in the process, the products of such disintegration would be in gaseous form, and would constitute an atmospheric envelope enclosing the undecomposed portion of the original mass of the Sun, hereinafter called the "nucleus." In the different stages of the Sun's development, the size of the atmosphere would depend partly upon the proportion of the nucleus, which had been converted by radioactive disintegration into simpler and lighter atoms, and partly on the temperature attained, since, other things being equal, the volume of a gas varies directly with its absolute temperature.

The development of the Sun would follow the general stellar mode of development, which has been previously described in Chapter II, pages 58-60. For illustrative purposes, this mode of development has been arbitrarily divided into eight stages, classified as to time relationships into three groups: past, present and future; as follows:

Past

Stage I.   A white dwarf star, having a relatively thin atmosphere, a disproportionately large nucleus, a density of about 60,000, and a surface temperature of about 12,000° K.

Stage II.   A normal blue star, with an enormously expanded atmosphere, a somewhat smaller nucleus than in the preceding stage, a density of probably somewhere between 0.1 and 0.2, and a surface temperature of about 15,000° K.

Stage III.   A normal white star, with an expanded atmosphere smaller in volume than in the preceding stage, a further diminished nucleus, a density of probably somewhere between 0.4 and 0.5, and a surface temperature of about 12,000° K.

Stage IV.   A normal pale yellow star, with an expanded atmosphere smaller in volume than in the preceding stage, a further shrunken nucleus, a density of probably about that of water, and a surface temperature of about 9,000° K.

Present

Stage V.   A normal yellow star, with an expanded atmosphere smaller in volume than in the preceding stage, a further shrunken nucleus, a density of 1.41, and a surface temperature of 6,000° K.

Future

Stage VI.   A normal red star, with an expanded atmosphere smaller in volume than in the preceding stage, a further shrunken nucleus, a density of probably about 1.60, and a surface temperature of about 3,000° K.

Stage VII. A dark, non-luminous star, in which much of the atmosphere has condensed to the liquid and solid states, forming a partly liquid, partly solid rock body (the lithosphere), which encloses at its center the much shrunken nucleus, and which is surrounded by a deep ocean (the hydrosphere), while that in turn is surrounded by a residual atmosphere, consisting of such gases as have remained uncondensed at the temperature attained. The density will probably be somewhere between 2 and 3, while the temperature will be about 290° K. at the surface of the ocean. In this stage the Sun, except for its far greater size, will somewhat resemble the planet Jupiter, to be later described.

Stage VIII. A "dead" star, in which the nucleus has entirely disintegrated and disappeared, thus eliminating all source of internal heat. It will consist of a solid rock body (the lithosphere), surrounded by a deep, solidly frozen ocean (the hydrosphere), but an atmosphere will be entirely lacking, as the gases constituting the atmosphere in the preceding stage will have condensed to solid form, at the temperature of space, to which that of the star will be slowly reduced. The density will probably be several times that of water.

The development of the Sun, as outlined above, is typical of the development of all of the stars, which, however, are in various stages, ranging from Stage I to Stage VIII. The high density, white dwarf star, which constitutes the initial stage in the Sun's development, should be distinguished from normal, low density dwarf stars in various stages of development, which represent stars of much smaller original mass than the Sun.

Under the Devolutionary Hypothesis, the Sun, in its present state, is assumed to contain at its center a relatively small, solid or liquid nucleus of high density, complex Q-atoms, which, around the periphery of the nucleus, are disintegrating, with the evolution of light, heat and other forms of radiation, into lighter and simpler atoms; and these lighter and simpler atoms have accumulated, since the commencement of the development of the Sun, to form a thick, hot, gaseous atmosphere surrounding the nucleus. Actual figures as to the size of the nucleus and the thickness and density of the surrounding incandescent gaseous atmosphere are not available; but, for purposes of illustration, assumptions can be made, which may not be too far in error, and which will permit some conclusions to be reached as to the probable internal constitution of the Sun. The actual energy output from the Sun's surface has been closely determined from the solar constant and the distance of the Earth from the Sun. The solar constant is the amount of radiation received from the Sun on a surface at right angles to the Sun's direction, just outside of the Earth's atmosphere, per square centimeter, and it has been found by measurement to be, on the average, 1.938 calories per minute; while the distance of the Earth from the Sun is about 93,000,000 miles. From these factors, the total energy emitted by the Sun has been calculated to be 9.054 x 10^{25} calories or 3.79 x 10^{33} ergs, per second.*

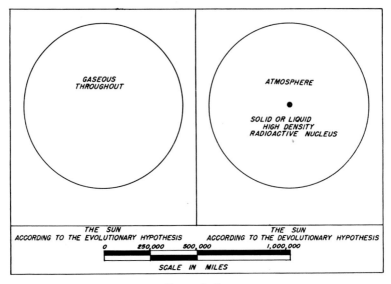

FIGURE 3 - 3

Illustrating diagrammatically the structure of the Sun, according to the contrasting Evolutionary and Devolutionary Hypotheses.

From the preceding figures, the weight of the radiation emitted by the Sun can be calculated by the Einstein mass-energy equation: E : MC^2 (Energy in ergs equals the mass in grams multiplied by the square of the velocity of light in kilometers per second.) The heat, light and other forms of radiation expelled from the surface of the Sun, amounting to 3.79 x 10^{33} ergs per second, weigh, according to

FOOTNOTE*: A calorie is the quantity of heat necessary to change the temperature of one gram of water 1° C. An erg is the energy expended when a force of 1 dyne acts through a distance of 1 cm. 41,860,000 ergs equal 1 calorie.

this formula, about 4,641,000 tons, and represent the energy by-products of the disintegration of the complex, high density Q-atoms, constituting the nucleus, into lighter and simpler atoms,—the latter being vaporized and joining the Sun's atmosphere, while the radiation struggles up through the Sun's atmosphere to escape from its surface into space. Assuming that the lighter and simpler atoms constitute about 99.97% of the original weight of the Q-atoms disintegrated, while radiation accounts for the remaining 0.03% (as compared with 0.02% radiation produced in the disintegration of uranium atoms), then the 4,641,000 tons of radiation emitted by the Sun each second (equivalent to 1.4646×10^{14} tons per year) indicates that 4.882×10^{17} tons of Q-atoms in the nucleus are disintegrating annually.

If it is assumed that the Sun is at present giving off only about 40% of the heat that it emitted during the period of its maximum heat evolution as a blue star, then the periphery or heat producing surface of the nucleus has probably been reduced accordingly, which would indicate that the nucleus has shrunk from its original diameter of about 24,800 miles to a present diameter of about 15,700 miles. The nucleus, consequently, has lost about 75% of its original mass; and if the density of the nucleus is assumed to be 60,000, then that of the Sun's atmosphere will be 1.05, to correspond to the Sun's present average density of 1.41. The present indicated loss of 4.882×10^{17} tons annually from the nucleus, through peripheral disintegration, indicates a radial shrinkage of the nucleus, amounting to about 1/7th inch annually. If this annual rate of shrinkage were constant, it would indicate that the disintegration of the Sun's nucleus had been in progress some 2,000,000,000 years, which would then represent the age of the Sun; but there is reason to suspect that the radial speed of peripheral disintegration of the nucleus, and accordingly the rate of its annual shrinkage, gradually diminishes, accompanying the increase of atmospheric pressure on the nucleus, due to the gradual transfer of mass from the disintegrating nucleus to the atmosphere of disintegration products surrounding it; and on such a basis, the above figure for the age of the Earth might be reduced to about 1,600,000,000 years. It is to be again strongly emphasized, however, that the preceding estimates are merely tentative and provisional, for illustrative purposes only, being based on assumptions, which, while regarded as reasonable, cannot be verified.

As previously described, the planets are supposed to be contemporaneous in age with the Sun, having been formed when the latter parted from a former sub-fragment of the Primordial Mass, then located in one of the two spiral arms of the Milky Way galaxy. The attraction of this sub-fragment raised two tidal arms on the Sun at the time of its separation. These tidal arms consisted of a number of individual blobs of Primordial Mass material, which eventually developed into planets; and some of these original planetary blobs, on parting from the Sun, also developed tidal arms, consisting of smaller blobs, which later formed the satellites. It seems probable that the Earth-blob was somewhat pear-shaped, and was in very rapid rotation, in the course of which it separated by fission into two parts, according to the process described on page 62, —the large end becoming the Earth and the small end the Moon, so that these two heavenly bodies are sister planets, instead of planet and satellite, respectively. As these sister planets revolved around their common center of gravity, the tides raised in the body of each by the attraction of the other tended to push them further and further apart, and to lengthen the periods of rotation of the Earth and of rotation and revolution of the Moon. Thus, it has been estimated that when they had become separated some 9,000 miles, the period of the Earth's daily rotation was not quite five hours long, while the period of the Moon's revolution was somewhat longer. This process of mutual repulsion is still taking place, and will continue until eventually the Earth keeps the same face always turned toward the Moon, just as the Moon does today with respect to the Earth, and each will rotate in a period equal to fifty-seven of our present days; but that will be millions of years hence.

The primitive planetary and satellitic blobs in due course went through exactly the same cycle of development as that described for the Sun, except that, their nuclei being smaller, the radioactive disintegration of these nuclei, although relatively somewhat retarded, approached completion much sooner, so that the planets and their satellites are at present in the seventh and eighth stages of their development. There is reason to believe that a small remnant of the original nucleus still survives within the Earth, where, as later described, it is responsible for current volcanic phenomena; but there are grounds for suspecting that a nucleus no longer exists within the Moon, where, although its face reveals abundant evidence of former volcanic activity, no eruptions have been seen during the period it has been under telescopic observation. Hence the Moon is probably in the eighth stage. In such case, a diameter somewhere between those of the Earth and the Moon marks the dividing line between those planets and satellites, in which disintegration of the nucleus is still taking place, and those in which it has ended. The Earth, Venus, Jupiter, Saturn, Uranus and Neptune still contain the vital spark, but Mercury, Mars, Pluto, all the Asteroids, and all the satellites, are probably finished worlds.

The sizes of the planets affect the extent of development of their atmospheres, and that in turn largely determines their habitability by organic life. The four planets nearest the Sun, comprising Mercury, Venus, Earth and Mars, known as the Terrestrial Planets, all have relatively thin atmospheres, or, in the case of Mercury, none at all; while the four largest planets, comprising Jupiter, Saturn, Uranus and Neptune, all have tremendously thick atmospheres, beneath which their solid bodies are permanently concealed. According to the kinetic theory of gases, the molecules constituting all planetary atmospheres are in rapid motion, constantly colliding with each other, and rebounding from such collisions like perfectly elastic spheres. The average velocity of these molecules (by which is meant the root mean square velocity, whose square is equal to the mean of the squares of the individual velocities) varies inversely as the square root of the molecular weight of the gas in question, and directly as the square root of the absolute temperature. For the most common gases, therefore, the value of this average velocity, in kilometers per second, at 0° C. (273° K.) is as follows:

	Molecular weight	Velocity		Molecular weight	Velocity
Hydrogen	2	1.84 km.	Nitrogen	28	0.49 km.
Helium	4	1.31 km.	Oxygen	32	0.46 km.
Water vapor	18	0.62 km.	Carbon dioxide	44	0.39 km.

At 100° C. and at 1,000° C. these velocities would be increased 17% and 116% respectively.

For each celestial body there is a certain surface velocity, called the velocity of escape, which depends on the gravitational attraction of its mass, and any molecule with a velocity in excess of this cannot be retained in the atmosphere of the body, but will fly off into space, while conversely any molecule with a smaller velocity will be restrained from escaping. Thus the velocity of escape is as follows for the Sun, the Earth and the Moon.

Sun: 618.   km. per second
Earth: 11.188 km. per second
Moon: 2.38   km. per second

However, while the average molecule, with a velocity less than the velocity of escape, will be retained, there will be certain molecules of higher speed in the outer portions of the atmosphere, where collisions between molecules are much fewer, which can escape, and, because of these, the planetary atmospheres will gradually waste away, unless the average velocity is not more than one fifth the figures shown above. For the Earth, therefore, an effective velocity of escape would be about 2.2376 km. per second at 0° C.

Unlike the Sun, which has sufficient gravitational attraction to retain all of the gaseous molecules released by the disintegration of its nucleus, the Earth would not be able to commence accumulating an atmosphere, until, in the course of its development, its surface temperature had cooled to about 1,500° K., when carbon dioxide molecules would be retained. Further cooling would capture the other atmospheric molecules, step by step, but hydrogen would not be permanently retained at a higher temperature than about 335° K. (62° C.), which helps to explain the small percentage of hydrogen in the Earth's atmosphere,—about 1/100th of 1%.

Other members of the Solar System, besides the Sun, the planets and the satellites, are meteors and comets. They have had very little influence on the development of the Earth, but merit consideration because of the information they provide as to the nature of the Earth's interior. Meteors vary in size from the finest dust to masses of many tons weight. Some of them may represent residual debris from the formation of the Solar System, which never assembled into larger masses; but, as shown by those meteors which have fallen to the surface of the Earth and have been found (meteorites), all the bigger ones show by their structure that they are fragments of larger bodies, and such bodies probably were comets, since comets have been known to split and disintegrate into swarms of meteors. Comets are solid bodies comparable in size with the Asteroids of the Solar System, and therefore probably ranging in diameter from one mile or less up to 500 miles; but, unlike the Asteroids, which revolve in a counter-clockwise direction around the Sun in orbits, that lie not far from the plane of the ecliptic, comets approach the Sun from all directions, and their orbits are highly eccentric and lie at all angles to the plane of the ecliptic. When comets approach the Sun closely, they become temporarily luminous, because of the volatile matter which is literally fried out of them by the heat of the Sun,—this luminosity being due partly to the reflection of sunlight from the gaseous molecules expelled from the comet's body, and partly from energy imparted to such molecules by the sunlight. Cometary orbits may be elliptical, parabolic or hyperbolic. If elliptical, the comet is, temporarily at least, a member of the Solar System, and it will sooner or later return; but if parabolic or hyperbolic, the comet will visit the Solar System but once, and then will vanish into interstellar space, never again to be seen from the Earth. An elliptical cometary orbit, however, may be changed into a parabolic or hyperbolic one, if the comet chances to pass too closely to one of the larger planets,— especially Jupiter,—in such a way that its speed is accelerated; and in that case the comet is literally flung out of the Solar System, never to return. Conversely, a stranger comet, visiting the Solar System for the first time, may have its parabolic or hyperbolic orbit changed into an elliptical one, if it happens to pass too closely to one of the larger planets, in such a way that its speed is retarded; whereupon it becomes domesticated, as it were, as a member of the Solar System, until such time as the situation is reversed, or, under the attraction of the Sun at close approach, it breaks up into a swarm of meteors. Some comets may originally have been Asteroids, whose planetary orbits were altered into cometary orbits, through the influence of Jupiter; while other comets were probably originally small planets of Asteroid size, which originated in some other stellar system of the Milky Way like the Solar System, and which were accidentally flung out of that stellar system through alteration of their orbits, because of too close approach to a large member of it, and thereafter became nomads, wandering through interstellar space, until they happened to come within range of the attraction of the Solar System, and so were drawn into it.

For the development of organic life in the Solar System, a number of limiting conditions must be met, which sharply restrict the possibilities. To be favored with the development of life, a planet must be sufficiently close to the Sun to receive enough heat to support and nourish life, but not so much heat as to destroy it. Organic life probably originates in the form of very minute one-celled plants (micro-plankton) in seas of enough volume, that they never dry up, and sufficiently warm that they never freeze but never become destructively hot. From these warm seas, organic life, by gradual adaptation to more rigorous and restricted living conditions, migrates landward. While a considerable degree of organic development can take place in the ocean, it is only on land that creatures of highest intelligence can evolve, and hence, for such an eventuality, land areas of sufficient size to be long-lived must also exist, contemporaneously with large oceans. The planet must have an atmosphere sufficiently thick to retain some of the warmth of the Sun's rays, and to provide a breathing medium, but not so thick as to totally exclude the sunlight, because sunlight is an indispensable requirement for the development of organic life. Through the agency of chlorophyll, one of the principal constituents of the leaves of plants, which acts as a catalyst, the energy of sunlight is utilized to decompose carbon dioxide in the atmosphere into carbon and oxygen, —the carbon being built into the bodies of plants, while oxygen is released, thereby providing a breathing medium for animals. To meet these several conditions, it is doubtful whether a planet, although properly situated as to distance from the Sun, so as to be warmed but not scorched by the Sun's heat, can be less than 5,000 miles or more than 12,000 miles in diameter,—the Earth's diameter being about 8,000 miles. For planets of smaller size than 5,000 miles diameter probably cannot acquire bodies of water of sufficient size and duration to generate and support primitive plant life, which is the ancestor of all more complex forms of plants as well as of animals, while in planets of larger size than 12,000 miles diameter the atmospheres would probably be too thick to admit sunlight. The only planets of the Solar System that can meet these conditions are the Earth and Venus. Mercury is too small to support an atmosphere, without which life cannot exist.

Mars has a thin atmosphere amounting in volume to probably somewhere between 10% and 30% as much per square mile of planetary surface as the Earth, with a pressure at the surface of between 4% and 12% of that which prevails here. The amount of oxygen per square mile of Mars' surface does not appear to exceed one tenth of 1% of that of the Earth, nor that of water vapor more than 1%. The Martian surface temperature must be well below freezing at sunrise and sunset, even at the equator, while the nights must be extremely frigid. The climatic conditions for the planet as a whole must be somewhat comparable to those existing on the summit of Mt. Everest (elevation 29,002 ft.) on the Earth, where no life exists. The most adverse feature of Martian surface conditions is the apparent entire absence of bodies of water,—at least those of any substantial size,—which could act as nurseries for organic life. Millions of years ago, when the Sun was hotter than now, Mars may have had a more genial climate, but it seems doubtful whether even then life could have originated on the waterless surface of that inhospitable planet.

Venus, with a diameter of 7,600 miles, is nearly the same size as the Earth, whose mean diameter is 7,918 miles, and it seems to have an atmosphere of comparable size and density, which, however, is always occupied by clouds, forming an impenetrable canopy below which the surface is always hidden. The planet probably contains both oceans and continents, somewhat similar in size and relative total area to those of the Earth. Being so much nearer the Sun and consequently receiving twice as much solar radiation as the Earth, the Venusian climate is probably very hot, humid and rainy, exceeding in this respect even the tropical rain forests of the Earth, while the oceans must be warm all over the surface of Venus. The question whether Venus contains organic life, therefore, probably depends chiefly on whether or not sunlight can penetrate through its perpetually cloudy atmosphere. If so, it may sustain plant life, with less probability of the existence of animal life, as suggested by the fact that the part of the atmosphere above the clouds seems to contain considerable carbon dioxide but no oxygen.

It is safe to conclude that no other planets of the Solar System contain living organisms. All the planets situated outwardly from Mars are too remote from the Sun to receive enough heat to have a surface temperature above freezing; in addition to which the Asteroids are too small to have atmospheres, while Jupiter, Saturn, Uranus and Neptune all have enormously thick atmospheres, through which sunlight would be unable to penetrate. Jupiter is probably fairly representative of these four planets, so that the following brief description of it should apply in general to the others as well. Jupiter has a mean diameter of 86,850 miles, or nearly eleven times that of the Earth, but with this difference that the given diameter of Jupiter is that of the outside of its atmosphere, while that of the Earth is the inside of its atmosphere or its surface. Since the atmosphere of Jupiter is very thick, this helps to explain the fact that, while the mass of Jupiter is 318.35 times that of the Earth, its density is less than a quarter of that of the Earth and only 1.33 times that of water. Jupiter must be composed of a partly liquid, partly solid core of rock minerals (lithosphere), surrounded

by an immensely deep ocean of water (hydrosphere), and that in
turn by a thick atmosphere. The distribution of Jupiter's volume
between these three divisions depends upon several unknown
factors, so that any estimate of its composition, such as that illustrated in Figure 3 - 4, can be regarded only as tentative and

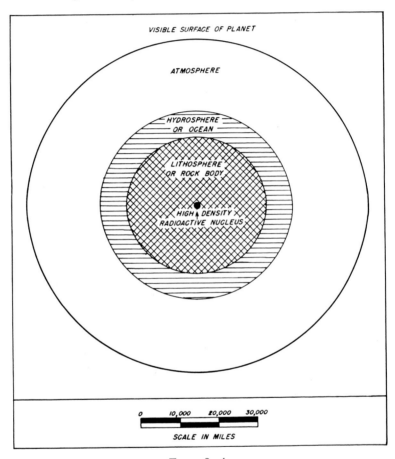

FIGURE 3 - 4

Diagrammatic cross-section of the planet Jupiter, on the basis of assumptions
as to the distribution of the mass of the planet between its atmosphere, hydrosphere and lithosphere. The size of the nucleus is probably much exaggerated.

provisional. Only two assumptions can be made with some degree
of probability: first, that its atmosphere probably consists largely
of hydrogen and helium, although only methane and ammonia have
so far been identified in its outer portions; and, second, that a con-

siderable remnant of its original nucleus still survives at the center of its lithosphere, and that in consequence volcanic activity is very intense. The other three major planets are probably similarly constituted, although the relative proportions of lithosphere, hydrosphere and atmosphere must differ somewhat, to account for differing densities.

Although life must be restricted to one or at most two planets of the Solar System, it may be widely dispersed throughout the Milky Way galaxy and the entire Universe as well, if, as seems probable, most of the stars were formed in a manner similar to the Sun, and hence, at the time of their parting from whatever fragments or subfragments of the Primordial Mass constituted their parents, they developed tidal arms, from which planetary systems later were formed. In such case, there may be millions of planets, in billions of stellar systems like the Solar System, containing plant and animal life.

CHAPTER FOUR

The Constitution of the Earth

The only parts of the Earth, which are exposed to direct human observation, are the air or atmosphere, the ocean or hydrosphere, and the surface of the crust or extreme outer portion of the solid body of the Earth or lithosphere. Surface exposures of the lithosphere are supplemented to some extent by exposures underground in mine workings or in drill-holes, but these latter are confined to the outermost three and a half miles of the crust. However, surface exposures of rocks, which have been formed at considerable depths, and have later, by earth movements, been exhumed and brought to the surface, suggest that to a depth of ten miles, at least, there is probably no great difference in the composition of the lithosphere. From the top of the atmosphere to a depth of ten miles below the top of the lithosphere, therefore, the following distribution of matter has been estimated:

TABLE III*

	Volume (cubic miles)	Density	Percent
Atmosphere (equivalent in water)	1,268,000		0.03
Hydrosphere (ocean)	302,000,000	1.027	6.58
Lithosphere (outer ten miles)	1,633,000,000	2.7	93.39
			100.00

The atmosphere is a mechanical mixture of gases, in which nitrogen and oxygen greatly predominate; and, except for the percentage of water vapor, which is concentrated in the lower part of the atmosphere, and rapidly decreases with height above the surface of the ground, the atmosphere, through the effect of convectional air currents, is a homogenous mixture up to a height of about 11

*FOOTNOTE: Tables III to VIII inclusive are quoted from the U. S. G. S. Professional Paper 127, "The Composition of the Earth's Crust," by Frank Wigglesworth Clarke and Henry Stephens Washington, 1924.

kilometers (6.85 miles) above sea-level. Above this bottom layer, which is called the troposphere, lies the isothermal region, called the stratosphere, in which there is almost no vertical convection, and the gases tend to lie in strata determined by their molecular weights. However, the troposphere constitutes about 77% by weight of the whole atmosphere, and as the composition above it changes but little up to 20 kilometers (about 12½ miles) above sea-level, below which 95% of the atmosphere lies, there is little error in assuming that the following composition of the troposphere by volume is representative of the entire atmosphere,—excluding water vapor. (Table IV)

TABLE IV			TABLE V	
			The composition of the hydrosphere or ocean is approximately as follows:	
Nitrogen	78.03%			
Oxygen	20.99%		Oxygen	85.79 %
Argon	.94%		Hydrogen	10.67 %
Water vapor	....		Chlorine	2.07 %
Carbon dioxide	.03%		Sodium	1.14 %
Hydrogen	.01%		Magnesium	.14 %
Neon	.00123%		Sulphur	.09 %
Helium	.0004%		Calcium	.05 %
Krypton	.00005%		Potassium	.04 %
Xenon	.000006%		Bromine	.008%
			Carbon	.002%
				100.00 %

The crust of the lithosphere, or solid body of the Earth, contains two different kinds of rocks, as to origin: (1) igneous rocks, which constitute the primary form; and (2) sedimentary rocks, which are secondary, and are derived from the igneous rocks through the processes of alteration, decomposition, disintegration, erosion, solution, deposition and precipitation. In the course of the formation of the sedimentary rocks, some salts have been leached and gathered in the ocean; but the weighted average composition of the sedimentary rocks will probably approximate very closely to that of the igneous rocks, from which they have been derived. While the sedimentary rocks are very conspicuous features of the surface of the Earth, and are very important in human economy, they are relatively insignificant quantitatively, when considered in relation to the Earth as a whole, because, although they may attain thicknesses as great as five miles or more in places, they are very thin or entirely missing over large areas of the surface of the globe, and the average thickness over the entire Earth probably does not exceed half a mile. They form, therefore, only a thin veneer upon the igneous rocks, which constitute the vast bulk of the Earth's substance. While there are many forms of sedimentary rocks and their altered or metamorphosed equivalents or derivatives, they may be represented, for purpose of comparison, by three general classes: (1) shales, which constitute about 80%; (2) sandstones, which constitute about 15%; and (3) limestones, which constitute about 5%. The average analysis of each class and of sedimentary rocks as a whole is as follows:

TABLE VI

	Shales 80% (Average of 78 shales)	Sandstones 15% (Average of 253 sandstones)	Limestones 5% (Average of 345 limestones)	Average
Silica (SiO_2)	58.11%	78.31%	5.19%	58.53%
Alumina (Al_2O_3)	15.40%	4.76%	.81%	13.07%
Ferric oxide (Fe_2O_3)	4.02%	1.08% ⎫		⎧3.37%
Ferrous oxide (FeO)	2.45%	.30% ⎬	.54%	⎬2.00%
Magnesia (MgO)	2.44%	1.16%	7.89%	2.51%
Lime (CaO)	3.10%	5.50%	42.57%	5.44%
Soda (Na_2O)	1.30%	.45%	.05%	1.10%
Potassa (K_2O)	3.24%	1.32%	.33%	2.81%
Water (H_2O) above 110° C.	3.66%	1.32%*	.56%*	3.16%
Water (H_2O) below 110° C.	1.33%	.31%	.21%	1.12%
Carbon dioxide (CO_2)	2.63%	5.04%	41.54%	4.94%
Titanium dioxide (TiO_2)	.65%	.25%	.06%	.56%
Phosphorus pentoxide (P_2O_5)	.17%	.08%	.04%	.15%
Sulphur trioxide (SO_3)	.65%	.07%	.05%	.54%
Sulphur (S)	....	....	.09%	....
Chlorine (Cl)	....	Tr.	.02%	Tr.
Baryta (BaO)	.05%	.05%	.00%	.05%
Manganese oxide (MnO)	Tr.	Tr.	.05%	Tr.
Strontia (SrO)	.00%	.00%	.00%	.00%
Lithia (Li_2O)	Tr.	Tr.	Tr.	Tr.
Carbon (C), organic	.80	....	....	.65%
	100.00%	100.00%	100.00%	100.00%

*Includes organic matter.

The average composition of the igneous rocks of the Earth's crust, both intrusive and extrusive, to a depth of ten miles below the surface, is estimated as follows:

TABLE VII

Average Composition of Igneous Rocks by Elements

Oxygen	46.59 %	Lead	0.002%
Silicon	27.72 %	Cobalt	0.001%
Aluminum	8.13 %	Boron	0.001%
Iron	5.01 %	Beryllium	0.001%
Calcium	3.63 %	Molybdenum	0.000n%
Sodium	2.85 %	Rubidium	0.000n%
Potassium	2.60 %	Arsenic	0.000n%
Magnesium	2.09 %	Tin	0.000n%
Titanium	0.63 %	Bromine	0.000n%
Phosphorus	0.13 %	Cesium	0.0000n%
Hydrogen	0.13 %	Scandium	0.0000n%
Manganese	0.10 %	Antimony	0.0000n%
Sulphur	0.052%	Cadmium	0.0000n%
Barium	0.050%	Mercury	0.0000n%
Chlorine	0.048%	Iodine	0.0000n%
Chromium	0.037%	Bismuth	0.00000n%
Carbon	0.032%	Silver	0.00000n%
Fluorine	0.030%	Selenium	0.00000n%
Zirconium	0.026%	Platinum	0.000000n%
Nickel	0.020%	Tellurium	0.000000n%
Strontium	0.019%	Gold	0.000000n%
Vanadium	0.017%	Iridium	0.0000000n%
Cerium, Yttrium	0.015%	Osmium	0.0000000n%
Copper	0.010%	Indium	0.00000000n%
Uranium	0.008%	Gallium	0.00000000n%
Tungsten	0.005%	Thallium	0.00000000n%
Lithium	0.004%	Rhodium	0.00000000n%
Zinc	0.004%	Palladium	0.00000000n%
Columbium, tantalum	0.003%	Ruthenium	0.00000000n%
Hafnium	0.003%	Germanium	0.00000000n%
Thorium	0.002%	Radium	0.000000000n%

The principal elemental constituents of the igneous rocks of the Earth's crust, both intrusive and extrusive, to a depth of ten miles below the surface, as listed in the preceding table, have been rearranged in the following table, chiefly in the form of oxides:

TABLE VIII

Silica (SiO_2)	59.12 %	Baryta (BaO)	.055%
Alumina (Al_2O_3)	15.34 %	Sulphur (S)	.052%
Ferric oxide (Fe_2O_3)	3.08 %	Chlorine (Cl)	.048%
Ferrous oxide (FeO)	3.80 %	Zirconium oxide (ZrO_2)	.039%
Lime (CaO)	5.08 %	Fluorine (F)	.030%
Soda (Na_2O)	3.84 %	Vanadium oxide (V_2O_3)	.026%
Magnesia (MgO)	3.49 %	Nickel oxide (NiO)	.025%
Potassa (K_2O)	3.13 %	Strontia (SrO)	.022%
Water (H_2O)	1.15 %	Cerium and yttrium oxides	
Titanium oxide (TiO_2)	1.05 %	($(Ce, Y)_2O_3$)	.020%
Phosphorus pentoxide (P_2O_5)	.299%	Copper	.010%
Manganese oxide (MnO)	.124%	Lithia (Li_2O)	.007%
Carbon dioxide (CO_2)	.102%	Zinc	.004%
Chromium oxide (Cr_2O_3)	.055%	Lead	.002%
			100.000%

One striking fact, revealed by the preceding table VII is that the nine most abundant elements constitute a total of about 99.25% of the outer ten miles of the Earth's crust, and that so many elements, which are considered essential for the needs of civilization,— including all of the common useful metals, except aluminum and iron,—are present only in very minute amounts.

Information as to the composition of the 99.24% of the bulk of the Earth, lying below the outer ten mile thick section of crust discussed in the preceding paragraphs, has been supplied in part by astronomical observations and physical experimentation; in part through the study of earthquakes; in part from the character of meteorites; and in part from the composition of certain rocks, now in the outer portions of the Earth's crust, which are believed to have originated at depths of more than ten miles below the surface.

An important factor in the study of the Earth's interior is the specific gravity of the Earth as a whole. This has been ascertained through application of the law of gravitation, which states that any two particles of matter attract each other with a force proportional to the product of their masses and inversely proportional to the square of the distance between them. By means of tests, whereby comparison was made of the attraction exerted by the Earth upon a body, with the attraction exerted upon the same body by another body of known weight at a known distance, the mass or total weight of the Earth has been determined; and, with the mass thus known, and the volume of the Earth determined by direct measurement of its surface dimensions, the specific gravity of the Earth, or its weight compared with that of an equal volume of water, has been ascertained. This proves to be about 5.517. But the average specific gravity of the rock formations constituting the outermost part of the Earth's crust has been found by direct test to average only about 2.7. It is evident, therefore, that the material composing the interior of the Earth must be much heavier than the average of the surface rocks. Observations and calculations, relative to the astronomical phenomenon known as the "precession of the equinoxes," suggest that, if there is nothing anomalous in the Earth's constitution, its density should increase roughly in proportion to the depth below the surface, as shown on Table IX. Tidal phenomena and other evidence indicate that, regardless of what the physical condition of its interior may be, the Earth, as a whole, behaves like a body with the rigidity of steel.

TABLE IX

Distance from the surface of the Earth to its center in tenths of its radius		Density	Pressure in atmospheres*
Surface	0.0	2.7	1
	0.1	3.8	197,000
	0.2	5.0	484,000
	0.3	6.2	849,000
	0.4	7.4	1,244,000
	0.5	8.6	1,806,000
	0.6	9.4	2,152,000
	0.7	10.1	2,566,000
	0.8	10.7	2,862,000
	0.9	11.0	3,060,000
Center	1.0	11.2	3,158,000

The gravity increases below the Earth's surface to a depth of 0.4 of the radius from the surface downward, at which point it is 2½ times as great as that on the surface. Below this point the gravity decreases until the center of the Earth is reached, where it is zero.

*FOOTNOTE: An atmosphere is the weight of the Earth's atmosphere, per square inch of its surface at sea-level, at a barometric pressure of 760 mm. of mercury, and equals 14.7 pounds per square inch.

The information from astronomical sources as to the steel-like rigidity of the Earth as a whole has been confirmed and amplified by data furnished by earthquake shocks. Delicately poised instruments called seismographs, located at many stations all over the world, have for many years automatically recorded the Earth tremors and vibrations caused by earthquakes, and the information obtained in this manner has proved of great value in diagnosing the nature of the Earth's interior. The accumulation of data by seismographs is favored by the fact that earthquakes are of frequent occurrence,— some 9,000 earthquakes annually, or about one an hour, being recorded. Of these, better than half are strong enough to be perceptible to human senses; while a little more than 1% are of sufficient intensity to damage buildings. There are, on the average, about twenty shocks a year comparable in strength to the San Francisco earthquake of 1906, in which, according to calculation, enough energy was released to raise a cubic mile of rock a vertical distance of about 6,000 ft. And yet this was by no means exceptionally severe, for several recorded earthquakes have been from ten to twenty times as powerful. Fortunately for the comfort of mankind, most of the violent earthquakes originate under the ocean, and hence do comparatively little damage to human life and property.

Earthquakes are classified, according to origin, as volcanic, tectonic or plutonic. As the name implies, those of the first kind are due to volcanic explosions or other causes related to volcanic forces, and hence are confined to regions of current or recent volcanic activity. They are shallow as to point of origin, and, although often spectacular in their effects, are relatively harmless. Tectonic earthquakes are caused by structural adjustments within the Earth's crust, and are usually manifested or accompanied by deformation, through faulting or warping of the surface above them. Their depth is much greater, on the whole, than that of volcanic earthquakes, and may extend as deep as 50 to 60 kilometers (about 30 to 35 miles), although by far the greater number of such earthquakes seem to originate within the upper 25 kilometers (15 miles) of the Earth's crust, and probably the majority occur at no greater depth than 15 kilometers (about 10 miles). But such earthquakes, although more frequent in regions of volcanic activity, are not confined to them, but may occur anywhere. At present, however, they are chiefly localized within two pronounced belts on the Earth's surface. Most of the destructive earthquakes of history belong to this class. Plutonic earthquakes are similar to tectonic earthquakes, except that they originate in the sub-crustal interior of the Earth, at depths ranging up to 700 kilometers (about 435 miles). Plutonic earthquakes originating below the bottom of the crust, up to a depth of about 300 kilometers (about 185 miles) from the surface, are classed as intermediate; while such earthquakes originating at depths of between 300 kilometers and 700 kilometers below the surface are classed as deep. In general, earthquakes decrease in frequency and strength with distance below the surface. Tectonic earthquakes account for about 85% of the average annual energy released, intermediate plutonic earthquakes for about 12%, and deep plutonic earthquakes for the remaining 3%; while the strength of the largest plutonic earthquakes is only about 10% of that of the largest tectonic earthquakes.

Regardless of the origin or nature of the different types of earthquakes, their effects are similar, in that they cause the propagation of vibrations in every direction through the surrounding rock, analogous to the tossing of a pebble in a pond, which causes the spreading of wavelets concentrically away from the point of disturbance. When these vibrations reach seismograph stations, the time of the occurrence, and the duration, intensity and direction of movement of them are automatically recorded; and when the observations at all affected stations are compared and correlated, the place of origin of the earthquake (called the focus, centrum or hypocentrum), and the point on the surface directly above (called the epicenter or epicentrum) can be determined,—often with a considerable degree of accuracy.

Two classes of vibrations or waves are generated by earthquakes. The waves of one class are structurally similar to sound waves in air; they are caused by the motion of the rock particles alternately forward and backward in a straight line from the source, causing an oscillation in the direction of the wave path. Such waves are called longitudinal or compressional waves. The waves of the other class progress in a different manner,—the particles moving forward and backward at right angles to the direction of the wave path. Such waves, which are structurally similar to light waves, are called transverse, torsional or shear waves. Longitudinal waves, as a class, may be transmitted through solids, liquids or gases; but transverse waves are limited to solids alone. This is an important distinction, since when transverse waves fail to pass through a certain medium or substance, it may reasonably be concluded that such medium is either liquid or gaseous. The longitudinal waves are about 75% faster than the transverse waves.

The two classes of earthquake waves are recorded on seismographs under three names. The first effects of an earthquake to be felt at a station are relatively mild tremors, caused by the longitudinal waves travelling from the focus by the quickest route through the body of the earth to the station. Such waves, being the first to arrive, are called the Primae or P waves. Next to come are the transverse waves, following the same route, and causing somewhat stronger tremors; they are called the Secundae or S waves. Lastly, there comes a series of more powerful vibrations, formed by waves of both classes, which have ascended from the focus to the surface above (epicenter), and thence travelled along the surface to the station. These are called the Main (M) or Long (L) waves, because of the fact that they are stronger and have longer periods. Most of the property damage, caused by earthquakes, is due to these waves.

If the shock has been sufficiently powerful, the first set of M waves, which has travelled from the epicenter to the station by the shortest path along the surface, is followed by another set, which has gone around the Earth in a contrary direction; and both sets may encircle the Earth more than once. Also the seismographic record may be still further complicated by secondary sets of P and S waves, due to refractions from the surface midway, or one-third and two-thirds the distance, between the focus and the station, and

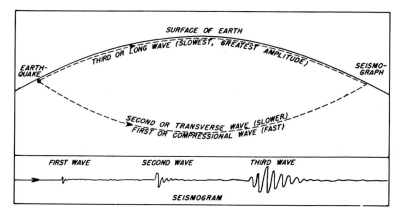

FIGURE 4 - 1

Illustrating diagrammatically the courses of the first, second and third earthquake waves. (After Nicholas Hunter Heck, "*Earthquakes*," Figure 40. Copyright 1936, Princeton University Press)

which are designated PP and SS waves in the first instance, and PPP and SSS waves in the second instance. The time interval between the arrival of the first P waves and the first S waves at a station provides a handy clue, in connection with the known velocity of each type of wave, to determine the distance of the focus. The representative seismogram, reproduced in Figure 4 - 1, shows the relative position and strength of the P, S and M waves in the earthquake recorded thereby.

Although the P (longitudinal) and S (transverse) waves travel from the focus of an earthquake to a surface station by the fastest route through the Earth's interior, this is not a straight line; instead the path followed is a curve, concave towards the surface. This is due to the fact that the physical and chemical condition of the Earth's interior is favorable for higher speed with increasing distance below the surface, up to a certain depth. The two principal conditions of the Earth's interior, which affect the velocity of earthquake waves, are elasticity and density. The velocity varies directly with the square root of the elasticity,—the more elastic substances transmitting impulses the faster,—and inversely as the square root of the density,—the denser and heavier substances exercising a retarding influence, because of their greater inertia, which the impulses must overcome. Hence increase of elasticity tends to accelerate the speed of the waves and increase of density to retard it; and since the speed of the waves increases with depth, the elasticity of the Earth's interior must increase faster than the density. By recording the time required for waves from a certain focus to reach different stations, the speed of the waves through different levels of the Earth's interior can be determined, and from this, in turn, the net ratio of the square root of the elasticity to the square root of the density at different depths below the surface can be calculated.

An important fact determined in this manner is that the general increase in this ratio, with greater depth below the surface, is not uniform, but is subject to relatively abrupt changes at certain levels, which are termed discontinuities. These discontinuities are not to be supposed to be sharp boundaries. Instead they are zones of probably a mile or more in thickness, within the first fifty miles below the Earth's surface, while with greater depth they may attain thicknesses up to ten miles or more. Their positions are recognized by changes in the direction and velocity of earthquake waves at such levels. The opinions of seismologists differ somewhat as to the number and positions of these discontinuities, partly because the evidence varies for different places of observation, due to differences in the character of the crust beneath them, and partly because of lack of agreement as to the interpretation of the experimental data. There is, however, general agreement as to the existence of two important discontinuities: one at a depth of from 40 to 60 kilometers (about 25 to 35 miles) below the surface, and the other at a depth of about 2,900 kilometers (about 1,800 miles) below the surface. Between the surface and the uppermost of these two major discontinuities at least one minor discontinuity has been generally recognized, while some observers claim that one or two others exist. If they do, however, they are probably local, and not globe encircling. Between the upper and lower major discontinuities, minor discontinuities have been reported by different observers to occur at depths of 120 kilometers (about 75 miles), 250 kilometers (about 155 miles), 400 kilometers (about 250 miles), 1200 kilometers (about 750 miles), 1700 kilometers (about 1055 miles) and 2450 kilometers (about 1520 miles), but only the last three of them have received general acceptance.

The following Figure 4 - 2 shows diagrammatically the change in the direction of earthquake impulses, which reveals the existence and indicates the position of the first major discontinuity. For simplicity of illustration, the one or more minor discontinuities between it and the surface have been disregarded.

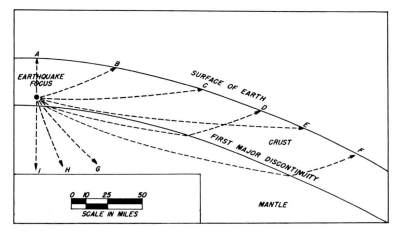

FIGURE 4 - 2

Illustrating diagrammatically the change in the direction of earthquake waves, when passing through the first major discontinuity. (After Reginald A. Daly, "Our Mobile Earth," Figure 65. Copyright, 1926, Charles Scribner's Sons, New York, N. Y.)

From the focus of an earthquake shock the impulses spread concentrically in all directions. The preceding figure shows the paths of movement of impulses in nine directions, spreading fanwise along a plane, and emanating from an earthquake focus, which, like the great majority of such foci, lies between the surface and the first major discontinuity. Wave-rays A, B, C and E traverse only the zone or layer above the discontinuity, and hence pursue undeflected paths to the surface, direct except for a slight curvature due to increasing density and elasticity of the material traversed with depth. Wave-rays D and F pass through the discontinuity, but are refracted in their courses, in exactly similar manner to the effect upon rays of light, when passing from one medium to another of different optical properties, and are again refracted as they leave the layer below the discontinuity to re-enter the zone between it and the surface. Rays G, H and I penetrate the Earth to great depth and emerge at the surface far from the focus. Similar effects, although weaker, are recorded at the minor discontinuities above and below the first major discontinuity.

Starting at the surface, the earthquake waves travel downwards with gradually accelerating velocity, until they reach a depth of from 10 to 40 kilometers (about 6 to 25 miles) below the surface, according to different localities and different observers,—the average speed in this distance being about 5.4 kilometers per second for the P or longitudinal waves and 3.3 kilometers per second for the S or transverse waves. At this level, which marks the first minor discontinuity, there is a sudden acceleration of velocity; and for the next 20 to 25 kilometers (about 12½ to 15 miles),—again varying according to different observers and different localities,—the P waves travel at an average rate of about 6.3 kilometers per second, and the S waves at an average rate of about 3.7 kilometers per second. At the bottom of this second zone lies the first major discontinuity, below which the velocity of the P waves increases suddenly to an average rate of about 7.8 kilometers per second and that of the S waves to an average rate of about 4.4 kilometers per second.

With further depth below the first major discontinuity, it is an increasingly difficult matter to determine the changes in velocity at the different minor discontinuities. It may be said, however, that the same principles apply, as quoted above,—that is, there is an acceleration of speed of the waves below each discontinuity, which is interpreted to mean that the underlying zone has a higher ratio

of the square root of the elasticity to the square root of the density
than the one above.

But when the second discontinuity is reached, at a depth of about
2,900 kilometers (about 1,800 miles), conditions are reversed. At
each discontinuity above, the wave velocities have increased and
the waves have been refracted towards the surface; but at this second
major discontinuity, the P or longitudinal waves, which have
attained at this level a speed of about 13 kilometers per second, are
suddenly reduced in speed to about 8.5 kilometers per second, while,
as shown in Figure 4 - 3, they are refracted *away* from the surface,

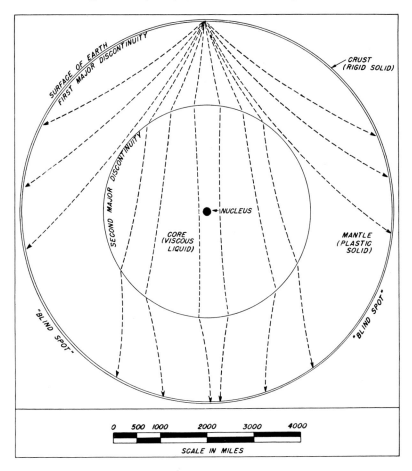

FIGURE 4 - 3

Illustrating diagrammatically the change in the direction of earthquake waves,
when passing through the second major discontinuity.

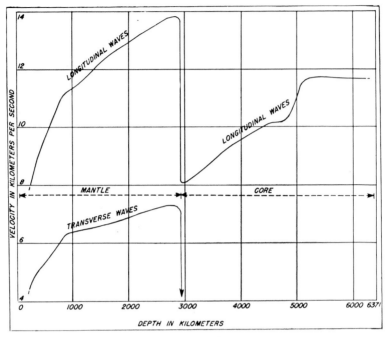

FIGURE 4 - 4

Illustrating graphically the speed of the longitudinal and transverse earthquake waves in the Mantle and the Core. (After Beno Gutenberg, "*Internal Constitution of the Earth*," Figure 42. Copyright, Dover Publications, Inc., New York, N. Y., 1951)

leaving between them and the nearest wave-rays, that pass through the body of the Earth above the second major discontinuity, an annular zone, distant from 7,000 to 10,000 miles around the surface from the epicenter, in which no longitudinal waves register at seismograph stations therein, forming the so-called "blind spot." The S or transverse waves are even more drastically affected, for they either stop entirely when entering this zone, or they come through so weakly as to be unrecognizable. The material encountered at about 2,900 kilometers depth (1,800 miles) continues nearly to the center of the Earth, and its effect upon both the longitudinal and transverse earth-quake waves suggests very strongly that it is some form of liquid.

The evidence supplied by earthquake waves, therefore, suggests that the interior of the Earth is divided, by two major discontinuities, into three great zones, of which the outermost zone, between the surface and the first major discontinuity, is termed the "Crust"; the second zone, between the first and second major discontinuities, the

"Mantle"; and the third zone, below the second major discontinuity, and extending nearly to the center of the Earth, the "Core." Their positions and relative thicknesses are shown in Figure 4 - 6.

Before attempting to interpret the meaning of the information provided by earthquake vibrations, and to deduce from this evidence the probable character of the interior of the Earth, it is necessary to consider three factors, which have a bearing upon the subject: (1) the pressure; (2) the chemical constitution of its interior; and (3) the temperature.

The cumulative weight of the superincumbent rock formations causes the internal pressure to increase progressively from the surface to the center of the Earth. At the surface, there is only the weight of the atmosphere, amounting to 14.7 pounds per square inch at the normal barometric pressure of 760 mm. of mercury at sea-level; while at the center the pressure increases over 3,000,000 times to about 23,200 tons per square inch. Since all substances are compressible to some extent, the increasing pressure with depth tends to squeeze substances into smaller volumes than they occupy on the surface, and this volume decrease is necessarily accompanied by a corresponding increase in density of the substance. The velocities of earthquake waves at different depths make it possible, by means of two formulae, to compute with a fair approximation to accuracy what this increase in density of the Earth's interior, due to compressibility alone, would amount to, at different depths down to the second major discontinuity, which is the greatest depth to which the velocity of earthquake waves can be measured with reasonable accuracy.

The square of the velocity of a transverse or S wave (V_s) is equal to the rigidity of the material traversed (R) divided by its density (D):

$$(V_s)^2 : \frac{R}{D}$$

The approximate density can be determined from a law formulated by LaPlace, that the density varies as the square root of the pressure. Knowing the velocity of transverse earthquake waves by measurement, the rigidity of the material traversed can be calculated from this formula.

The square of the velocity of the longitudinal or P waves (V_p) equals the reciprocal of the compressibility of the material traversed (K) plus 4/3rds of its rigidity (R), divided by its density (D):

$$(V_p)^2 : \frac{K + 4/3R}{D}$$

Inserting in the equation the value for the rigidity as determined by the preceding formula, and knowing by measurement the velocity of the longitudinal earthquake waves, the reciprocal of the compressibility and hence the compressibility itself (1/K) can be calculated.

Assuming an average specific gravity of 2.7 for the rock formations at the surface, pressure alone would increase this to a specific gravity of about 4.2—an increase of about 55%—at the level of the second major discontinuity, which is about 45% of the distance from the surface to the center. But in order for the density of the entire Earth to equal 5.517, as it has been determined to be, the density of the interior, if it increased at a uniform rate from the surface to the center, should be about 8.0 at the second major discontinuity. It is evident from this discrepancy, therefore, that some other factor or factors, besides compressibility due to pressure, must influence the density of the Earth. There are three such possible factors: (1) an increase in the proportion of the heavier elements with depth; (2) an increase in the formation of heavier minerals with depth; and (3) the existence, at the center of the Earth, of a nucleus of high density atoms, inherited from the Sun.

If the Earth was once in a molten condition, as there is some reason to believe, it is to be expected that there would have been, to some extent, a gravitative segregation of its constituents,—the lighter predominating near the surface and the heavier with depth; and there are two lines of evidence to support the belief in some increase in the proportion of heavier material with depth, due to such gravitative segregation.

One of them is the distribution of rocks in the visible portion of the Earth's Crust. The igneous rocks of the Crust are chiefly of two types,—granite and basalt. Among the visible intrusive rocks in the Earth's Crust, the granites and granodiorites, with an average specific gravity of from 2.66 to 2.74, occupy more than twenty times the area of all other intrusives combined; but among the visible extrusive rocks, basalt, with an average specific gravity of about 2.95, has at least five times the volume of all other extrusives combined. Since the deep plutonic masses, from which the basaltic extrusives originated, are very scantily revealed by erosion, it is safe to conclude that they lie at a lower level in the Earth's Crust, on the average, than the granites and granodiorites, and hence that in the Earth's Crust, at least, there is an increase in density from about 2.7 at the surface to 2.95 near its bottom.

The other line of evidence has to do with the meteorites, which fall from the heavens upon the Earth's surface, and which are believed, as previously discussed, to represent the fragments of heavenly bodies of small size, such as asteroids or comets, which approached too closely to larger bodies and were torn to pieces by their attraction. Their ultimate origin is supposed to be comparable to that of the Earth, so that in composition they would resemble it. Those meteorites, which survive their fall, and have been found and recognized, are divisible as a whole into three classes: "siderites," which consist almost wholly of an alloy of nickel and iron in metallic form, with very small percentages of a few other elements; "aerolites," which consist chiefly of ferro-magnesian silicates, and approach the composition of peridotites; and "siderolites," or the so-called "stony meteorites," which are intermediate in character between the other two. All three types grade into one another, but they are not equally abundant, since only about 3% of those meteorites, which have been observed to fall and have been recovered, have been siderites. Representative analyses are shown in the following table.

TABLE X

	Siderites Iron Average of 318	Siderolites Stony Average of 125	Aerolites Achondritic Average of 20
Iron (metallic)	90.67%	11.46%	1.18%
Nickel (metallic)	8.50%	1.31%*	0.33%
Cobalt (metallic)	0.59%	0.05%	0.04%
Oxygen		36.02%	42.05%
Silicon		18.41%	23.00%
Aluminum		1.39%	3.26%
Iron (silicate)		12.88%	12.33%
Magnesium		13.54%	10.91%
Calcium		1.65%	5.09%
Sodium		0.59%	0.50%
Potassium		0.17%	0.22%
Titanium		0.01%	
Chromium		0.28%	0.31%
Manganese		0.14%	0.18%
Sulphur	0.04%	1.98%	0.54%
Phosphorus	0.17%	0.06%	0.06%
Carbon	0.03%	0.06%	
	100.00%	100.00%	100.00%

*Includes some NiO

It is not to be supposed that the average composition of those meteorites, which have been found and recognized, is representative of the heavenly bodies, from which they originated. The tough and massive nickel-iron meteorites are far more apt to survive their passage through the atmosphere and impact upon the Earth's surface than the frailer and less homogenous aerolites, and they are also far more apt to be found and identified, because of their striking difference from terrestrial rocks, some of which latter the aerolites more or less resemble. It seems probable, therefore, that the proportion of metallic nickel-iron in all the meteorites roaming through space is much less than it is in those meteorites, which have been found and identified on the Earth's surface. Metallic nickel-iron of terrestrial origin, similar in all essential respects to that occurring in meteorites, exists in a few localities on the Earth's surface, while peridotitic rocks, similar to the nonmetallic part of meteorites, are not uncommon. All such material, however, seems to have been originally deep-seated, and there is reason to believe that, with increasing depth below the surface, minerals similar to those composing meteorites become more abundant, and eventually identical.

On this assumption, the principal chemical constituents of the Earth's body at different levels may originally have been somewhat as follows,—subject to some subsequent mixing in the Earth's Crust, through intrusive action and assimilation, as later described. (pp. 161-163).

TABLE XI

	Crust Top third	Crust Middle third	Crust Bottom third	Mantle Top ten miles Perido-	Mantle (remainder) and Core
	Granitic	Dioritic	Diabasic	titic	Meteoric
Silica (SiO_2)	70.47%	57.56%	51.45%	50.20%	45.54%
Alumina (Al_2O_3)	14.90%	16.90%	15.64%	6.33%	4.49%
Ferric oxide (Fe_2O_3)	1.63%	3.20%	3.91%	....	....
Ferrous oxide (FeO)	1.68%	4.46%	7.93%	16.27%	16.68%
Magnesia (MgO)	.98%	4.23%	5.90%	18.64%	19.93%
Lime (CaO)	2.17%	6.83%	9.11%	7.30%	4.82%
Soda (Na_2O)	3.31%	3.44%	3.13%	.69%	.78%
Potassa (K_2O)	4.10%	2.15%	.98%	.28%	.23%
Manganese oxide (MnO)	.13%	.13%	.21%	.23%	.21%
Titanium dioxide (TiO_2)	.39%	.85%	1.48%	....	.02%
Phosphorus pentoxide (P_2O_5)	.24%	.25%	.26%	.06%	.11%
Iron, metallic (Fe)	....	....	....	....	6.32%
Nickel, metallic (Ni)	....	....	....	....	.82%
Cobalt (metallic) (Co)	....	....	....	....	.05%

There would be, of course, all degrees of gradation between any two neighboring columns.

Another factor in the increase in the density of the Earth with depth is the probable formation, under the greater pressure that accompanies greater depth, of heavier minerals than exist near the surface. Certain molecules, occurring in nature, are polymorphic, having two or more mineral forms, chemically identical, but differing as to crystal form and specific gravity,—the lighter and less symmetrical forms tending to occur nearer the surface, and the heavier and more symmetrical forms at greater depth. Thus tridymite, a hexagonal form of silica, with a specific gravity of 2.28 - 2.33, favors the near surface, but tends to give way with depth to quartz, of identical composition, rhombohedral in form, with a specific gravity of 2.653 - 2.654,—a volume decrease of 14.24%. Aggregates of minerals forming rocks also change under pressure to form new compounds. Thus granite under great static pressure changes into ortho-gneiss of density greater than the original rock,—there being a shrinkage of 16% in volume when the orthoclase in the granite passes over into quartz and muscovite in the ortho-gneiss. It is probable, therefore, that under the tremendous pressure existing at great depths in the Earth's body, below the surface, molecular rearrangements result in the formation of new minerals and mineral aggregates, of relatively high specific gravity and great complexity, which are entirely unknown in the Crust of the Earth.

A fourth factor, in increasing the density of the Earth with depth, is the probable existence, at the center of the Earth, of a nucleus of high density atoms, inherited from the Sun, according to the Devolutionary Hypothesis (p. 83). Such high density atoms may be direct survivals of the high density atoms, with an estimated specific gravity of about 60,000, that are assumed to have constituted the Primordial Mass, from which the Sun and its planets, with their satellites, are supposed to have descended, or they may represent the partial disintegration of such original high density atoms into intermediate atoms of somewhat less density but still very high as compared with the atoms composing the bulk of the Earth's mass.

In summary, therefore, the increase in the density of the Earth with depth below the surface is probably due to four factors:

(1) The compressibility of all forms of matter under pressure.

(2) An increase in the proportion of some of the heavier elements—notably iron and nickel—and a decrease in the proportion

of certain of the lighter elements—notably silicon and aluminum—with depth.

(3)   Molecular changes, resulting in the formation of denser molecules and aggregates of molecules under pressure.

(4)   The survival, at the center of the Earth, of a nucleus of undisintegrated or but partially disintegrated Sun-inherited high density atoms.

Certain astronomical data throw light on the probable relative importance of these four factors. With respect to the four interior planets of the Solar System,—Mercury, Venus, Earth and Mars,—together with the Moon, it is possible because of the thinness of their atmospheres, or, in the case of Mercury and the Moon, the entire absence of any, to determine with approximate accuracy their "bare-body" dimensions, or the sizes of their lithospheres, from which their volumes can be figured. From this information, together with their masses, which are determined by their gravitative effect upon each other and upon other members of the Solar System, their densities can be calculated. If these five members of the Solar System all inherited from the Sun, at the time of their separation from it, the same kind of original high density atoms, as assumed under the Devolutionary Hypothesis, then the average chemical composition should be approximately the same in each case, but the larger ones, being more highly compressed because of greater pressure in their interiors due to larger size, and also containing larger surviving nuclei of undisintegrated high density atoms, should have the higher densities. The following table of the diameters and densities of these five heavenly bodies, arranged in order of increasing size, shows that this is the case.

TABLE XII

	Diameter in miles	Density Water : 1	Diameter Earth : 1	Density Earth : 1
Moon	2,160	3.33	0.272	0.604
Mercury	3,000	3.73	0.378	0.68
Mars	4,200	3.95	0.530	0.71
Venus	7,600	5.21	0.959	0.94
Earth	7,917	5.52	1.000	1.00

To further illustrate the relationship between the diameters and densities of these five heavenly bodies, they have been plotted on the accompanying graph, from which it will be noted that the density

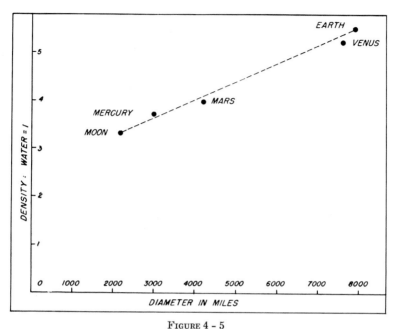

FIGURE 4 - 5

Illustrating graphically the relationship between the diameters and densities of the Moon, Mercury, Mars, Venus and the Earth.

is almost a direct function of the diameter. This suggests that the factors of dominant importance in determining density are pressure and the size of the nucleus, and that the increase in the proportion of the heavier elements with depth, outside of the nucleus, is of much less consequence. This is further evidenced in the special case of the Moon. With an average density of 3.33, it is obvious that if, as seems likely, the density of the rocks at its surface is about the same as that of the Earth's surface formations (2.7) or but slightly less, there cannot be any very large proportion of metallic nickel-iron, with a specific gravity of about 8, in its composition,—probably not more than 6% to 7%. The Earth is doubtless similarly constituted. The relatively low density of the Moon also suggests that it contains no nucleus of high density atoms at its center,—any such nucleus, that it may once have had, having entirely disintegrated. This conclusion will be supported by other evidence, to be considered later.

One further feature, which affects the interior condition of the Earth, is to be considered,—its temperature. It has been well established by numerous tests that the rock temperatures of the

Earth's Crust increase with depth below the surface, indicating that heat is escaping from the interior of the Earth to its surface, where it is dissipated by radiation. The amount of heat thus escaping can be determined when the rate of increase of temperature with depth, called the temperature gradient, and when the heat conductivity of the rocks composing the Earth's Crust, are known.

The most dependable records of temperature gradient are those obtained from deep mines and drill-holes, which afford the greatest range in temperature, and where results are least affected by surface conditions. The gradient exhibits considerable variation from place to place, being usually steepest in regions of current or recent vulcanism, or in mountainous areas, particularly those of geological youth; and it tends to be flattest where opposite conditions prevail. The range between different places is very large,—the steepest recorded gradient being nearly eleven times that of the lowest gradient. Thus, at the high end, the temperature gradient at Lakeview, Oregon, where there is a hot spring of probably magmatic origin, is $1°$ C. per 9.7 meters depth; the gradient at Thermopolis, Wyoming, where there is a similar hot spring, is $1°$ C. per 13.1 meters depth; and the gradient at the Tintic Standard mine in the State of Utah, where the rock temperature registers $103°$ F. at a depth of 1450 feet below the surface, is about $1°$ C. per 15 meters depth. Conversely, at the low end, the average temperature gradient of eleven deep mines in the Province of Ontario, Canada, is $1°$ C. per 92.5 meters depth, while the average gradient of twenty-two deep mines in the Witwatersrand district of South Africa is $1°$ C. per 107.3 meters depth. There are all degrees in between these extremes; but an average of 46 deep mines and drill-holes,—all but one deeper than 600 meters and most of them in excess of 1,000 meters depth,—is $1°$ F. per 63.4 ft. ($1°$ C. per 34.8 meters), and it is customary to assume, for purposes of calculation, an average world-wide gradient of $1°$ C. per 33.33 meters, or $3°$ C. per 100 meters of depth.

The conductivity of a substance is measured by the quantity of heat in calories, which a slab of the substance 1 cm. thick will transmit per square centimeter of area, in one second, when a temperature difference of $1°$ C. is maintained on opposite faces. There are large differences between the conductivities of different substances,—gases as a class having the lowest and metals the highest. Thus the conductivity of dry air is 0.00006, while that of silver is 1.006,—about 17,000 times as much. The various types of rocks that compose the Earth's Crust have, as a class, intermediate conductivities,—granite varying from 0.00513 to 0.00601 and basalt from 0.00345 to 0.00409. These figures are for rocks in a dry state; when moist their conductivity may be increased from 10% to as much as 100%. In nature most of the rocks are moist, and allowance must be made for that fact; consequently, for purposes of calculation, the average conductivity of the rocks composing the Earth's Crust may be assumed to be 0.007.

With such a conductivity, and an average temperature gradient assumed to be 3° C. per 100 meters, or 0.0003° C. per centimeter, the amount of heat escaping at the surface of the Earth would be calculated at .007 x 0.0003° C. or 2.1×10^{-6} calorie per second per square centimeter of the Earth's surface,—the calorie being the amount of heat required to raise the temperature of one gram of water 1° C.,—while the total amount of heat thus escaping would amount to 1.07×10^{13} calories per second or 3.37×10^{20} calories per year, from the entire surface of the Earth. This result is probably too small, since relatively few mines have been opened or drill-holes sunk in regions of current or recent vulcanism, where the temperature gradient is higher than elsewhere, because of the relative proximity of bodies of molten rock to the surface; and, to correct this deficiency, it is estimated that the above amount should be increased 10%, to 3.71×10^{20} calories per year.

Allowances must also be made for substantial heat contributions to the atmosphere made in connection with various phases of vulcanism. Thus, assuming the several hundred active volcanoes on the Earth,—an active volcano being defined as one which has erupted at least once in historic times,—to expel annually, on the average, a total of one cubic mile of lava and equivalent in ash and other by-products, at an average temperature of 1,010° C., which eventually cools down to 10° C., the heat emitted in this cooling down process would amount to 0.12×10^{20} calories. The fact that many volcanoes have expelled, in a single eruption, much more that one cubic mile of lava and by-products is believed to be justification for this assumption:

Volcanoes	Lava and ash expelled in a single eruption
Crater Lake, Oregon, U.S.A. (prehistoric)	10.75 cubic miles of ash, equivalent to 6 of lava.
Frambruni, Iceland (prehistoric)	5.58 cubic miles of lava and ash.
Veidivatnahraun, Iceland (prehistoric)	10.36 cubic miles of lava and ash.
Eldgja, Iceland (about 830 A.D.)	2.25 cubic miles of lava. .35 cubic miles of ash.
Laki, Iceland (1783 A.D.)	2.95 cubic miles of lava. .50 cubic miles of ash.
Krakatau, East Indies (1883 A.D.)	Ash equivalent to 4.00 cubic miles of lava.

The expulsion of lava, ash and other by-products during a volcanic eruption is always accompanied by the escape of heated magmatic gases in large volume. Thus, during the eruption of Vesuvius in 1906, which occupied a period of eighteen days, the lava and ash expelled are estimated to have yielded 3.6×10^{17} calories of heat, while the accompanying gas emitted is estimated to have yielded 1.23×10^{17} calories of heat. But the emission of gas from the crater, although at a much reduced rate, preceded and followed the actual eruption for many years, during periods of semi-dormancy. So, accepting Vesuvius as a typical volcano, and making allowance also for the heat emission from hot gases issuing from fumaroles and from the hot water of thermal springs, distributed over the Earth's surface, it seems reasonable to assume that the heat contributions from all of these supplementary sources is at least half of that contributed by lava, ash and other products, and therefore amounts to 0.06×10^{20} calories annually for all the active volcanoes on the Earth.

The total amount of heat escaping annually from the interior of the Earth, therefore, is estimated as follows:

By conduction through the Earth's Crust:	3.71×10^{20} calories.
In lava, volcanic ash and other volcanic by-products:	$.12 \times 10^{20}$ calories.
In volcanic gases from craters and fumaroles, and in hot water from hot springs:	$.06 \times 10^{20}$ calories.
Total annual heat emission:	3.89×10^{20} calories.

There are three possible sources of this escaping heat:

1. The cooling down of the Earth from a previous molten condition.

2. The generation of heat in the Earth's body,—chiefly in its Crust,—due to the radioactive disintegration of atoms of uranium, thorium, the $_{19}K^{40}$ isotope of potassium and others, scattered through it.

3. The generation of heat at the Earth's center, due to the disintegration of radioactive, high density atoms, constituting a central nucleus, inherited from the Sun.

1. Before the discovery, in recent years, that the atoms of certain elements, present in small amounts in the rocks of the Earth's Crust, were disintegrating, with the evolution of heat, it was universally supposed that the heat loss, described above, was due solely to the cooling of the Earth from an originally molten condition. Starting with the assumption that the Earth was originally liquid throughout, with an average temperature of 3,900° C., Lord Kelvin many years ago calculated that it would cool to its present temperature in somewhere between 20,000,000 and 40,000,000 years; and this result has recently been confirmed by other physicists*, who have obtained a figure of 22,000,000 years. However, since this period of time is far less than the age of the Earth is now believed to be, from several lines of evidence, it would appear that the cooling of the Earth from a high primitive temperature was, for all practical purposes, completely accomplished long ago, and that the present emission of heat from the Earth's surface is due wholly to other causes.

2. Within the past fifty years it has been discovered that the atoms of a few elements,—chiefly uranium, thorium and the $_{19}K^{40}$ isotope of potassium,—which occur in small quantities in the Earth's body, are radioactive, and are disintegrating slowly, with the evolution of heat in small amount; and investigation has shown that these radioactive elements appear to be associated chiefly with rocks containing much silica, alumina, potassium and sodium, such as granite, syenite, trachyte and phonolite, and are least abundant in those rocks, which are relatively low in those constituents, such

---

*FOOTNOTE: "Heat Conductivity," by L. R. Ingersoll, O. J. Zobel and A. C. Ingersoll, p. 99. McGraw-Hill Book Company, Inc., New York, N. Y., 1948.

as basalt, gabbro, peridotite, etc. The heat production of uranium, thorium and potassium[40] has been measured as follows:

	Per gram per second
Uranium	2.45×10^{-8} calorie
Thorium	7.0×10^{-9} calorie
Potassium[40]	2.55×10^{-13} calorie

Since the amounts of these elements present in rocks are very variable, even in rocks of the same type, and since the content is very small, ranging, in the case of uranium and thorium, from 1/1000 of 1% to 1/1,000,000 of 1%, it will be appreciated that the determination of the content of these elements in rocks of different type is subject to so large a factor of error, as to make the results open to some doubt. It is not surprising, therefore, that the figures obtained by different investigators differ considerably. There seems to be, however, general concurrence as to the relative heat production of these elements in different kinds of rocks, as per the following list, in which acidic igneous rocks have been taken as unity:

Sediments	0.6
Acidic igneous rocks	1.0
Intermediate igneous rocks	0.65
Basic igneous rocks	0.35
Ultrabasic igneous rocks	0.005

Stony meteorites show about the same heat production as terrestrial ultrabasic rocks, which they resemble, while iron meteorites show much less, down to none at all. It will be noted that the heat production is concentrated in the first four types of rocks, which are confined wholly or almost wholly to the Earth's Crust, and that the heat production of the ultrabasic igneous rocks, which constitute the sub-crustal body of the Earth, is very low. The average thickness of the sedimentary rocks is estimated at 0.5 mile, but there is no direct evidence as to the thicknesses of acidic, intermediate and basic igneous rocks in the Earth's Crust, which probably vary somewhat from place to place. Accordingly it is not possible to calculate, with any degree of confidence, the probable heat production of uranium, thorium and potassium[40] in the Earth's Crust, but if it was substantial, it should be manifested by certain phenomena.

Thus, it would be reasonable to expect that, other things being equal, large areas of dominantly acidic rocks, such as granite, should show a higher heat production than areas, in which there are great surface thicknesses of basaltic lava flows, which suggest the presence of large intrusive masses of basic igneous rocks at relatively shallow depth in the Earth's Crust; but such does not appear to be the case. Thus, it might be expected that the thermal gradients would be relatively steep in the Witwatersrand district of South Africa, where the formations consist of silicious sediments underlain by granite, and in the Province of Ontario, Canada, where the terrain consists principally of granite in large masses; but, as a matter of fact, their thermal gradients are among the lowest on record. Investigation of temperature gradients in various parts of the world suggests that they bear no obvious relationship to the kinds of rocks probably constituting the Earth's Crust as such localities, but are chiefly influenced by the probable present degree of proximity of intrusive igneous rocks to the Earth's surface.

If heat production were much greater proportionately in the Earth's Crust than in its sub-crustal interior, as would follow if uranium, thorium and potassium[40] were the sources of this heat, the temperature gradient should flatten out so much below the Crust, that the temperature of the Earth's Core should not be high enough to liquefy it, especially in view of the fact that the melting point of diabase, selected as a representative igneous rock, has been found, within experimental limits, to rise directly with the pressure. Calculations suggest that, on this basis, the temperature at the Earth's center might be somewhere between 2,000° C. and 4,000° C. But the evidence of earthquake waves points strongly to the conclusion that the Earth's core is liquid throughout, so that at its boundary, some 1,800 miles below the surface, the temperature gradient must have overtaken the pressure gradient, and therefore be steeper than the latter. Even if the low average temperature gradient of 1° C. per 107.3 meters prevailing in the Witwatersrand District of South Africa should apply, this would require a temperature in excess of 27,000° C. at the Core boundary, with a still higher temperature at the Earth's center.

Furthermore, if the heat production were so much greater proportionately in the Earth's Crust than in its sub-crustal interior, the Crust should expand proportionately more than the sub-crustal interior, and hence the interior should not exert pressure upon the bottom of the Crust. But, as discussed in the following chapter, the evidence is strong that the Earth's interior is expanding more than the Earth's Crust, and that all of the phenomena of vulcanism and orogeny (mountain building) are directly due to the upward pressure which the Earth's interior is exerting on the bottom of the Crust.

In conclusion, therefore, it appears that the heat production in the Crust and the sub-crustal interior of the Earth, due to the disintegration of uranium, thorium and potassium[40] that it contains, must be only a fraction,—possibly not more than 10%,—of the total heat emission of the Earth, which latter has been estimated at 3.89 x 10[20] calories annually. In such case, the amounts of these elements in the body of the Earth may have been greatly overestimated; and considering the minuteness of these amounts, such an error would be quite excusable. Thus one estimate of the amount of uranium in the Earth's body ranges from .0003 of 1% in acidic rocks to .0000015 of 1% in ultrabasic rocks, and, for the amount of thorium, from .001 of 1% in acidic rocks to .000005 of 1% in ultrabasic rocks. The great difficulty of determining closely such extremely small amounts is obvious, and the results may be subject to so large a factor of error as to seriously compromise calculations based on them. Furthermore, the figures are based on a relatively small number of samples, which do not adequately represent the entire surface of the Earth, while also all of the samples have been taken only from the Earth's surface, and there is no direct information available as to the content of these elements in the underlying formations.

3. If, as appears probable, the amount of heat generated within the Earth's body by the disintegration of certain known radioactive elements contained within it, such as uranium, thorium and potassium[40], supplies only a fraction of the total heat emission from the Earth's surface, then the balance of this heat emission must originate from some other source; and the most plausible identification of this source is that it is a mass of atoms of great complexity and weight, situated at the Earth's center. This mass— hereinafter referred to as the Nucleus—is assumed to be spherical in shape, solid or liquid throughout, relatively small in size —probably not exceeding a mile in diameter,—and intensely radioactive on its surface, where it is disintegrating into simpler atoms such as constitute the rest of the Earth's body, with a large evolution of heat, which, migrating outwardly through the Earth's body, keeps the Core in a liquid condition and eventually escapes at the Earth's surface. It is assumed, as discussed in the preceding chapter, that the Earth was originally composed entirely of this material, in the form of a sphere about 600 miles in diameter,

derived anciently from the Sun, but ultimately stemming from the Primordial Mass. The Nucleus would be too small to be indicated by earthquake waves, and the evidence as to its existence, aside from the general principles of cosmogony according to the Devolutionary Hypothesis, rests partly on its relationship to volcanic and orogenic phenomena, as described in the following chapter; partly on the fact that the heat emission from the surface of the Earth seems to be too great to be explained simply by the disintegration of known radioactive elements confined principally to the Earth's Crust; and partly by the fact that a relatively high heat emission from the Earth's center would seem to be necessary to maintain the material of the Core in a liquid form, as indicated by earthquake waves. The evidence at hand as to the condition of the interior of the Earth, and the conclusions drawn therefrom, may now be summarized.

There are two major discontinuities in the body of the Earth,— one at a depth of about 40 to 60 kilometers (25 to 35 miles), and the other at a depth of about 2,900 kilometers (about 1,800 miles) below the surface. There is little reason to doubt that the cause of each such discontinuity is a relatively abrupt change in the physical condition of the body of the Earth at such level.

The first major discontinuity marks the bottom of the zone known as the "Crust," or, as it is sometimes called, the "Zone of Fracture." Within this uppermost zone, which constitutes about 2.3% of the volume of the Earth, but probably only about 1.1% of its mass, the rocks are chiefly in the form of rigid and brittle solids, whose strength is usually sufficient to resist the pressure, due to gravity, to which they are subjected, and, if they eventually yield to stresses, they do so largely by fracturing. In composition the rocks composing this zone vary from silicious to basic, and the arrangement of such rocks in the Crust is roughly stratiform according to density, ranging from silicious rocks at the top to basic rocks at the bottom. The proportion of the different kinds is unknown, but it may be assumed that acidic rocks, such as granite, occupy the top third; intermediate rocks, such as diorite, the middle third; and basic rocks, such as gabbro and diabase, the bottom third, as a whole. However, there has been so much mixing and so much penetration of the underlying basic rocks upward into the overlying silicious rocks, due to volcanic activity, as later discussed, that it may not be far amiss to consider the Crust as rather heterogenous in composition. Since the Crust differs in character at different points, its thickness also differs, which accounts for variations in the position of the first major discontinuity beneath different places on the Earth's surface. The great majority of earthquakes originate in the Crust, because the rocks composing it tend to resist stresses, until such stresses have accumulated to a point where they exceed the strength of the rocks, whereupon the latter yield suddenly, with a violent shock.

Below the first major discontinuity there is a sudden acceleration of velocity of both types of earthquake waves, the longitudinal and the transverse, indicating an increase in elasticity; and the zone lying between this discontinuity and the second one is called the "Mantle" or the "Zone of Flowage." In this zone, which occupies about 81.5% of the volume of the Earth and probably contains about 73.1% of its mass, the rocks are in the condition of plastic solids, whose strength as a whole is less than the pressure due to gravity, to which they are subjected, so that they usually yield to Earth stresses by permanent deformation without fracturing, brought about by slow molecular readjustment. An illustration of a plastic solid at the surface is afforded by a glacier, which, under the influence of gravity, moves slowly down hill, often over relatively gentle grades, by means of such molecular readjustments within its mass. In the Crust there are some types of rocks, such as shales, which flow under light pressure at relatively shallow depths, and it is probable that in that zone an increasing proportion of the rocks yield by flowage with increasing depth, until at the bottom of the zone and the top of the Mantle the entire mass yields in that manner. Earthquakes in the Mantle are much rarer than in the Crust, because the rocks tend to yield slowly to stresses, and it is only when the stresses accumulate faster than the rocks can conform to them by flowage, that earthquakes originate in that zone. The Mantle probably consists exclusively of ultrabasic rocks and is fairly uniform and homogenous throughout, although there may be some increase in the small content of metallic nickel-iron with depth. The minor discontinuities in the Mantle and the Crust are probably due to relatively abrupt physical modifications in the condition of the material, without any change in its chemical composition.

Below the second major discontinuity, which lies at a depth of about 2,900 kilometers (1,800 miles) below the surface, there is a large and abrupt drop in the velocity of the longitudinal earthquake waves, which are transmissible through both solids and liquids, while the transverse earthquake waves, which are transmissible only through solids and not through liquids, either disappear entirely at this level or are so much weakened that they are not recognizable. This fact suggests that at this level the temperature has increased sufficiently to overtake the melting point of the material, which has been greatly increased by the corresponding increase in density due to pressure; so that in the zone below this discontinuity, which is called the "Core," and which occupies about 16.2% of the Earth's body but constitutes about 25.8% of its mass, the rocks have changed in physical condition from a plastic solid to a viscous liquid. The principal difference between these two physical states is that the former yields slowly under sufficient pressure, while the latter yields slowly under any pressure, due to greater relaxation of the bonds between the mole- cules. In both the "Mantle" and the "Core," however, the material is under such pressure that it possesses qualities far different from what it would exhibit at the surface, under the same temperature. The material of the "Core" probably consists wholly of ultrabasic rock, with more or less admixture of metallic nickel-iron, and it is probable that it is fairly uniform in character throughout, and closely approximates in average composition that of the Mantle, except for its uppermost portion.

In addition to the three zones of the Earth previously described, —the "Crust," the "Mantle" and the "Core,"—there is thought to be a fourth, the "Nucleus," which is enclosed in the "Core" and occupies the center of the Earth. It is believed that the Nucleus is spherical in shape; that it is of entirely different character from the material composing the other three zones, and consists largely of high density atoms, (about 60,000 specific gravity), which are of extra-terrestrial origin, having been inherited from the Sun, although originally derived from the Primordial Mass (Q-atoms); that it is disintegrating radioactively on its periphery, by stages, into ultimate end products, which are simpler atoms, like those composing the Earth's body; that this disintegration is accompanied by the evolution of heat, which is responsible for the liquid physical state of the Core, and accounts for most of the heat emission from the Earth's surface; and that a result of this peripheral atomic disintegration of the Nucleus into lighter and simpler atoms is an expansion of the volume of the Earth, which accounts for vulcanism and orogeny. Within the Nucleus, immediately underlying the Core, there is probably a zone, of greater or less thickness, of intermediate decomposition products of the original Q-atoms.

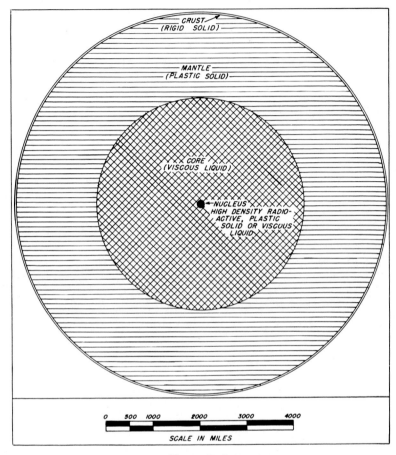

FIGURE 4 - 6

Diagrammatic cross-section through the center of the Earth. The size of the Nucleus is greatly exaggerated.

The part of the annual heat emission of the Earth, which is assumed to originate from the Nucleus, has been estimated at 3.50×10^{20} calories. This is only a very minute fraction, amounting to 1.225×10^{-13}, of the Sun's annual heat emission. If the heat emission in each case is proportional to the area of the heat-radiating surface,—with due allowance for a decline in the rate of peripheral disintegration, due to the pressure exerted on the Earth's Nucleus by the weight of the accumulation of disintegration products surrounding it,—then the Earth's Nucleus has probably wasted away from an original diameter of some 600 miles to a present very small size,—possibly not larger than a sphere of one mile diameter. Also, since the disintegration of Q-atoms takes place in steps or stages, similar to the mode of disintegration of uranium atoms set forth on page 14, and the complete disintegration may take a very long time, the present Nucleus of the Earth may be composed largely, if not chiefly or even wholly, of intermediate disintegration products, from which the heat emission would be at a much smaller rate than from the original Q-atoms. In such case, the Earth's Nucleus probably constitutes only a very minute fraction of 1% of the Earth's total volume, and also, despite its very high density, only a fraction of 1% of its total mass; while the future life of the Nucleus, until it completely disintegrates and disappears, will probably not exceed only a few million years.

The evidence furnished by earthquake waves forms the basis for the description of the first three zones, which latter seem to be generally accepted by scientists; but the Nucleus is a recent concept, advocated to explain certain geological phenomena, which can not logically be accounted for under any former hypothesis. It awaits, therefore, scientific consideration and approval.

CHAPTER FIVE

The Cause of Vulcanism and Orogeny

The Earth, while slowly approaching an ultimate completely static condition, which is the equivalent of death to suns, planets and satellites, is not aging quietly. Instead its surface bears evidence of two conflicting activities at work, one constructive, the other destructive. The constructive activities consist of vulcanism and orogeny (mountain building), which are indicated, in the case of vulcanism, by the growth of volcanoes, which sometimes reach full stature in less than a single century, and, in the case of orogeny, by the much more leisurely growth of non-volcanic mountains, which is so slow that it can be measured only by geological time scales. The destructive activities are those of air and water in the form of erosion, which endeavors to level all the land areas and to submerge them beneath the ocean; and the fact that it has never yet in the past succeeded in this attempt provides proof that the constructive activities are still much the stronger. The constructive activities are the surface manifestations of still surviving active agencies, deeply seated within the body of the Earth, and intimately connected with its past history.

The discussion as to the constitution of the Universe and the constitution of the Solar System, in two previous chapters, has been prompted by the need to discover the cause of vulcanism and orogeny in the Earth's body; and since this cause must be some force, which is inherent in the nature of the Universe, it has seemed likely that it could most readily be identified outside of the Earth. However, the original clue to the nature of this cause has been supplied by terrestrial evidence: the known existence, within the Crust of the Earth, of chemical elements—usually of relatively considerable atomic complexity and high specific gravity, such as uranium and thorium,—which are spontaneously disintegrating into lighter and simpler elements, and whose disintegration cannot be arrested, retarded, accelerated or in any way affected by any means within human control. This suggests that these elements,—and others even heavier and more complex, whose existence deep within the body of the Earth is suspected but cannot be directly proved,— are in unstable equilibrium and hence not in their normal environment, but are the chance survivors of a former different state of matter. This circumstance leads ultimately, through a long chain of evidence and reasoning, to the cause of vulcanism, but before it can be developed and explained, it will be necessary to disprove an older hypothesis, which stands in the way, and which, while theoretically unsound and while lacking proof, has long enjoyed popular favor and scientific esteem.

Thus, it is frequently stated in text-books of geology and astronomy that the Earth has been contracting in size since its formation, and that this process is still continuing. The line of reasoning, by which this conclusion is reached, is that the Earth was once molten; that heated substances contract as they cool; and hence that the Earth must have contracted in cooling from a molten to a solid state, and, since it is still emitting heat from its interior, by conduction through its crust, it must still be cooling and hence still contracting. In support of this conclusion, it has been pointed out that the Earth's crust is in places much folded, and it is claimed that this condition could have been brought about only as incidental to the accommodation of an unshrinking solid crust to a shrinking plastic or liquid interior. An analogy, which has frequently been cited in this connection, is the wrinkling of the skin of a withered apple, or of the epidermis of an elderly person, which, in each case, is due to the shrinkage of the sub-cutaneous substance. There are, however, two major errors in the premises in the above chain of reasoning, which invalidate its conclusion.

The first error lies in the assumption that the Earth is still cooling from an original molten condition. Without disputing the probable fact that, in an earlier stage of its history, the Earth was molten or largely molten, the Earth must long ago have cooled from such a condition, as discussed on page 119 of the preceding chapter; and the present emission of heat from the surface of the Earth is due wholly to the generation of heat by disintegrating radioactive elements in the Earth's body, in consequence of which the Earth's interior temperature is now remaining constant. There being no present cooling, there can be no present shrinkage due to that cause.

But even if the Earth were still cooling from a former molten condition, the assumption that the Earth's body would be contracting as it cooled constitutes the second error. It is true that, as a general rule, the cooling of a pure substance is attended by a reduction in volume, whether in the same physical state, as a gas, liquid or solid, or whether in the course of a physical change from a gas to a liquid or a liquid to a solid. There are a few exceptions, the most notable of which is water, which contracts from 100° C. down to 3.9° C., but expands as it is further cooled from 3.9° C. to 0° C., and also expands, when transformed from water at 0° C. to ice at the same temperature. Experiments by Carl Barus and others have shown that most rock-forming minerals and their aggregates into rocks follow the general rule, while in the solid state; and the coefficient of expansion of the average rock has been measured by T. Mellard Reade as 0.00002838 and by Whitman Cross as 0.0000199, per 1° C., which is therefore the rate at which contraction would occur on cooling in the solid state. But the above applies only in the cases where a substance in the liquid state contains no gases in solution; for a liquid can hold a much greater volume of gases in solution than can the same substance in the solid state; and hence in the transformation from a liquid to a solid, the excess gases are expelled as the liquid congeals, and the total volume of the resulting solid substance plus that of the expelled gases is usually greater than that of the original liquid, while containing the gases in solution. For most substances containing gases in solution, when in liquid form, therefore, the change from the liquid to the solid state is accompanied by an expansion of the volume of the resulting products,—solid plus freed gases,—which more than offsets any contraction of volume due to cooling, when in the liquid or solid state, so that the net result of the transfer from the liquid to the solid state is an expansion in volume.

A common illustration of this fact occurs in the manufacture of blocks of artificial ice from water containing air in solution, as all natural water does. The ice first forms on the surface of the water and against the sides and bottom of the metal container, thus entrapping the air and preventing its escape; and, as congelation progresses inward, the air is forced to migrate before it into the water still remaining liquid in the center, and when the latter eventually solidifies, the air separates as multitudes of small bubbles along a median plane in the center of the block of ice. Allowing for the expansion of water from 3.9° C. to 0° C., and of water at 0° C. when transformed into ice at the same temperature, the resulting block of ice is larger than the original water, by the volume of the entrapped and separated air bubbles,—the amount of the increase in bulk due to this cause depending upon the extent of the original aeration of the water.

A similar example is provided by the lead and copper smelting industry, in the course of the solidification of the molten slag, which, as it issues from the furnaces, always contains a considerable amount of dissolved gases; and this example is the more illuminating, because of the resemblance of furnace slag, which is actually an artificial lava consisting of melted rock, to natural lava. When such furnace slag is transferred to a slag pot for transportation to the slag dump, the following sequence of events takes place, if the potful of slag is allowed to completely solidify. A solid crust quickly forms over the surface of the slag in the open pot, while the slag next to the sides of the pot soon solidifies, thus sealing off the escape of the gases; and as they are expelled from solution by the progressive congelation of the slag inwardly from the top and sides of the pot, they are compelled to move toward the still liquid center. Coincidently, the pressure in the liquid interior, due to the accumulation of gases therein, increases until it is sufficient, either to detach the solidified crust from its adherence to the sides of the pot and to float it to a higher level, or to rupture this crust of solidified slag and to force upwards through the cracks some of the still liquid slag of the interior, which spreads over the surface in a thin, quickly congealing layer. (The analogy of this process to fissure eruptions, whereby molten lava rises non-explosively through fissures on the flanks of basaltic volcanoes, and spreads therefrom over the surface as lava flows, is obvious). The continued inward progress of solidification of the slag, with attendant separation of its contained gases and their forced migration towards the center, may create sufficient inner pressure for these phenomena to be repeated several times, before the potful of slag completely solidifies. When a solidified potful of slag is broken, its center will be found to consist of a spongy mass of slag, containing numerous large and small cavities and vesicles, occupied by the separated gases; and these cavities are encrusted by pyrogenetic crystals, similar in their origin and occurrence to the natural crystals, which line miarolytic cavities in igneous rock. The transformation of the slag from a liquid to a solid, therefore, is accompanied by an expansion of volume,—the space occupied by the solidified slag with its contained gas vesicles being greater than that previously filled by the molten slag with its dissolved gases.

Another manifestation of the process of expansion of gas-charged liquids during solidification is afforded by the explosions,

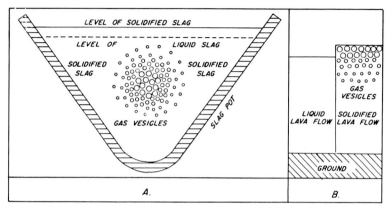

FIGURE 5 - 1

A. Diagrammatic cross-section of potful of solidified blast furnace slag, showing the concentration of expelled gases in the center, resulting in an expansion of volume of the solidified slag over the original volume in the liquid state.

B. Illustrating diagrammatically the expansion of volume of solidified lava over that of the original liquid lava, due to the separation of magmatic gases during solidification and their concentration near the top of the lava.

which result when masses of copper matte, blister copper, lead bullion, furnace slag and other similar substances containing gases in solution are dropped, when molten, into water and thus suddenly chilled. These explosions have been attributed to other causes, such as the rapid evolution of steam from the surrounding water, or from chemical reactions such as the dissociation of steam into hydrogen and oxygen and their immediate explosive recombination; but such explanations do not harmonize with the bomb-like fragmentation of the material, and the random dispersal and high velocity of flight of the fragments, which indicate that the propelling impulse was not external to the molten masses, but came from within them. The further circumstance that the explosions are not peculiar to any certain chemical substances, but result whenever molten substances containing gases in solution are abruptly chilled, suggests that the essential conditions are the presence of gases in solution, together with sudden external cooling, causing the formation of a solid outer shell enclosing a still liquid interior,—the solid shell, as the internal pressure mounts due to the progressive separation of the dissolved gases, being eventually ruptured with explosive violence. The violence of the explosion in such a case will depend upon the amount of the dissolved gases and upon the strength of the material; for evidently the greater the original gas content, the higher will be the resulting internal pressure; while if the material possesses considerable tenacity and strength in the solid state, it will resist rupture until the internal pressure mounts to such a degree that, when it finally exceeds the strength of the enclosing shell, the yielding will be paroxysmal. Thus copper matte, which is tough and strong, causes greater explosions than copper furnace slag, which is brittle; while liquid blister copper, which has a higher gas content than molten lead, is more dangerous, when suddenly immersed in water.

All igneous magmas contain gases, as indicated by the gases given off during volcanic eruptions, and as shown by chemical analyses of solid igneous rocks, which always reveal the presence of gases, together with some liquids and solids which were in gaseous form when the rock was molten,—the total actual and latent gas content usually ranging from 1% to 5% by weight. The result is that igneous rocks, solidifying at the surface and at shallow depth below it, usually show more or less vesiculation, or the formation of bubble cavities, due to the expansion of the contained gases and their separation from the magma in the form of gas bubbles distributed through it. All this results in an expansion of volume, exemplified in an extreme case by pumice, which often has a specific gravity only half that of water and so floats on the surface,—its volume being over five times as great as that of the liquid magma, from which it was derived. Under greater pressure, such as exists at depth below the Earth's surface, the expansive power of the contained gases, when released as the magma solidified, would be restricted to minute or even microscopic gas vesicles, just offsetting the shrinkage in the solid material, so that the net result would be a constant volume.

Having pointed out the theoretical flaws in the hypothesis that the body of the Earth is shrinking in volume, accompanying its supposed cooling, it is now in order to consider the visible evidence in the Earth's Crust, which has a bearing on the question. If molten igneous magma shrunk during the process of congelation, some indication of this effect should be manifested by the formation of shrinkage cracks. Such cracks should separate intrusive bodies from the formations which they intrude, and should be distributed generally throughout the masses of the intrusive. It is reasonable to expect that the shrinkage cracks might vary in frequency in different igneous masses, or that they might be larger or more numerous in certain portions of an igneous mass that cooled under somewhat different conditions than the other portions; but at least they should be distributed with some approach to uniformity, under approximately similar conditions, and should not occur in certain portions while being absent from other portions, because, while the rate of cooling and the strength of the rock may affect the spacing and size of the cracks, a certain number of shrinkage cracks must be formed, irrespective of the rate of cooling, if a certain reduction in the volume of an intrusive is to be effected. Except to a very limited extent, shrinkage cracks are not to be expected to occur in the intruded rocks, even where they have been heated to a high degree of temperature, since such rocks would presumably return to their former volume after the cooling of the intrusive, and there would not have been any permanent change in them, as might be the case with the intrusive. Only in instances where the volume of the intruded rocks had been permanently affected through chemical or physical changes due to the intrusion might shrinkage cracks be possibly formed on cooling.

Shrinkage cracks always exhibit a peculiar and characteristic pattern, which distinguishes them from joint cracks and fault fissures. The contractile impulses operate from numerous closely spaced, somewhat uniformly distributed centers, and form polygonal blocks, separated from one another by narrow cracks, which have random courses, continue in one direction for a short distance only, and do not cross one another. There is no movement along the cracks, which simply result from a gaping or pulling apart of their walls, and hence the material on the opposite sides of such a crack always matches. The polygonal blocks thus formed rarely exceed two feet in diameter, where in rock formations. This netlike pattern, which is always the same, whatever the medium in which the shrinkage cracks occur, and whether due to cooling or drying, is illustrated by the polygonal mud tiles, which pave the floor of a dry pond, or by the network of minute cracks that form in chinaware, which has been heated and suddenly cooled.

Joint cracks, which are formed by compressive, tensile or shearing stresses in the Earth's Crust, resemble shrinkage cracks in their narrowness, in the fact that no differential movement takes place along them, and in the usual regularity and uniformity of their distribution, where they occur. Unlike shrinkage cracks, however, joint planes may occur in any kind of rock,—igneous, metamorphic or sedimentary,—and may pass without interruption from one kind of rock to another. Joint planes may cross one another, and they

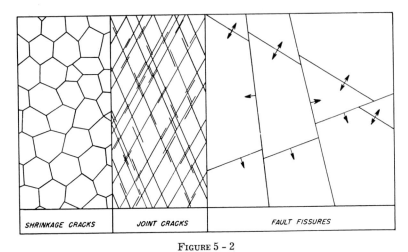

SHRINKAGE CRACKS   JOINT CRACKS   FAULT FISSURES

FIGURE 5 - 2

Illustrating diagrammatically the different patterns formed by shrinkage cracks,
joint cracks and fault fissures.

maintain fairly straight and definite courses, while they may persist
individually for considerable distances. The spacing of joint planes
is quite variable, and may range from a few inches to many feet.
The principal feature, which distinguishes joint planes from shrinkage cracks, is the notable difference in their patterns. Joint planes
occur in sets, in which they are more or less parallel; and where
there are two or more sets, crossing each other, they tend to create
blocks of rhomboidal shape, quite different from the polygonal blocks
formed by shrinkage.

The difference in character between fault fissures—or their
mineralized equivalents, fissure veins,—and shrinkage cracks is
more considerable than between joint planes and shrinkage cracks.
A fault fissure is caused by local stress in the Earth's Crust, resulting
in its rupture, with the formation of a fissure, along which, on one
or both sides, more or less movement takes place. A distinctive
feature of a fault fissure, therefore, is that the walls on opposite
sides of the fissure do not match. In the movement along a fault
fissure during its formation, the abrasion of one wall upon the other
usually creates attrition products, such as gouge or fault breccia,
or causes the formation of fault striae, although they are not always
present in faults of slight displacement. A fault fissure usually
follows a relatively straight course throughout, unless subjected
to some special deflecting influence; and it is often of considerable

extent, both on strike and dip. Fault fissures may traverse all formations of greater age, irrespective of character or origin, passing
across igneous contacts without interruption and usually without
deflection. In any one district, they are apt to occur in one or more
groups, each having a common direction. They have no geometrical
order or regularity, like shrinkage and joint cracks, and are very
irregularly distributed, being concentrated in certain areas and
sparse in others.

Joint planes are of almost universal distribution throughout
the upper part of the Earth's Crust; fault fissures are much less
abundant, but still are common; while shrinkage cracks are notably
scarce, being confined to certain lava flows, beds of volcanic ash,
and near-surface sills and dikes,—particularly those of basaltic
composition. In those formations, columns of polygonal cross-section
are developed, which are usually at right angles to the surfaces of
such formations, and hence tend to be vertical in lava flows, beds of
volcanic ash, and sills, and to be horizontal in dikes. These columns
are best developed next to the surfaces of the formations, and
diminish in strength inwardly, often completely disappearing in the
interior. Joint planes and fault fissures are formed by different
stresses than can be attributed to the Earth's shrinkage, while such
unmistakable shrinkage cracks as occasionally are visible in lava
flows, beds of volcanic ash, and near-surface sills and dikes are
caused only by surface or near-surface chill, at the time of solidification, and do not represent shrinkage of the Earth's body as a whole.
As a matter of fact, the vast majority of dikes, sills and intrusive
masses, particularly those which are deep-seated, show no visible
evidence whatever of any contraction in volume having accompanied
their solidification. In most cases their contacts with the intruded
formations are not marked by cracks, but instead are welded,—
often so tightly that an attempt to cleave the rock along the line of
suture fails. Occasionally cracks or fissures due to jointing or
faulting may form along sections of the plane of contact, and thus
be suggestive of shrinkage cracking, but these can usually be identified by application of the criteria previously described, in which
event the suspected shrinkage crack will either prove to be one of
a general system of joints of regional distribution, traversing intrusive and intruded rocks indiscriminately, or will be found to be
a fault fissure, marked by evidences of movement along it, and of
much later age than the intrusive. The mere occurrence of a fissure
in an intrusive mass cannot properly be considered to be even

presumptive evidence of genetic relationship and of approximately contemporaneous age, since in the usually lengthy time interval before most intrusive masses are revealed by erosion, ample opportunity is afforded for stresses of subsequent origin to cause the formation of joints and faults. In some mining districts, where faults or veins are conspicuously concentrated within or in close proximity to certain igneous masses, this relationship formerly was confidently interpreted as indicating that such faults or veins were true contraction fissures, directly resulting from the shrinkage of the igneous mass in cooling; but in nearly all such cases it can be shown that the faults or veins are not symmetrically disposed with regard to the igneous mass, as they should be if they were caused by shrinkage; that they traverse both intrusive and intruded rocks impartially; and that they fault and displace the intrusive rocks equally with the intruded rocks and hence must have been formed after the consolidation of the former. In many cases it can be shown that the veins also traverse formations younger than the intrusive, and therefore must have originated at a much later period and be due to entirely independent causes.

A more plausible application of the theory of the contraction of the Earth's body, due to cooling, to the formation of fault fissures and fissure veins traversing intrusive masses acknowledges such structures to have been formed by Earth stresses in the customary manner, but attributes the faulting to the irregular subsidence of the area in question due to mass contraction of the intrusives at great depth. In rebuttal, it should be pointed out that the periphery of an intrusive mass cools more quickly than its interior, and hence should more conspicuously exhibit indisputable evidence of shrinkage through the formation of shrinkage cracks, if shrinkage actually had taken place, and that if no such evidence is visible in the peripheral areas exposed by erosion, it is hardly logical to assume that the deeper portions of the mass would manifest a different tendency. Areas of igneous intrusion are frequently areas of extensive faulting for the reason that in such regions the igneous intrusions have weakened the Crust, so that subsequent deformative stresses, which are resisted to a considerable extent where the Crust is strong and unbroken, are most apt to produce their maximum effects in such weakened areas. Igneous intrusion is often accomplished in stages, separated by intervals of repose, so that renewed movement produces new stresses, which often cause fracturing of the superincumbent formations. Where an intrusive

has caused the doming of the intruded formations, as is quite frequently the case, faulting is a logical consequence, unconnected with
any question of contraction of the mass in cooling. Fault fissures
and fissure veins are of such universal distribution throughout rocks
of all types, and are in so many cases obviously due to causes
independent of and long subsequent to the intrusion of igneous
masses, occurring in the vicinity, that there is little reason to mistake
them for true contraction effects. In conclusion it may be summarized that the polygonal cracking of rocks is evidence of contraction, but that joint planes and fault fissures are due to other
causes and have no connection with shrinkage phenomena; while
the formation of polygonal shrinkage cracks in those surface or near
surface igneous formations, to which they are confined, is purely
a local phenomenon, due to quick chilling, and provides no support
whatever in favor of the hypothesis of the shrinkage of the entire
Earth in volume, due to cooling from a former liquid state.

It is now appropriate to consider in some detail the evidence
provided by faults and folds in the Earth's Crust, as supporting or
opposing the shrinkage hypothesis. There are three types of faults:
(1) normal faults; (2) reverse or thrust faults; (3) transcurrent
faults. The general direction of movement along the plane of a
normal fault results in the footwall side rising relatively to the
hangingwall side; the general direction of movement along the
plane of a reverse or thrust fault causes the hangingwall side to
rise relatively to the footwall side; while the general direction of
movement along a transcurrent fault is horizontal. However, the
direction of movement along a fault plane is frequently more or
less oblique, and therefore consists of two components,—a vertical
component or dip-slip; and a horizontal component or strike-slip.
Such a fault is of somewhat intermediate nature, but one component
is almost always dominant and determines the classification of the
fault.

Normal faults are extremely abundant and of universal distribution in the Earth's Crust, although they vary in frequency in different
areas, being more common in regions of crustal deformation than
in regions where the Crust has been but little disturbed. They are
not entirely absent from any area of considerable size, however, and
hence must be considered to be manifestations of world-wide stresses.
The significant feature of normal faults is that they result in an
expansion of the Earth's surface, as shown in Figure 5 - 3, and hence
must be due to tensile stresses in the Earth's Crust, as opposed to

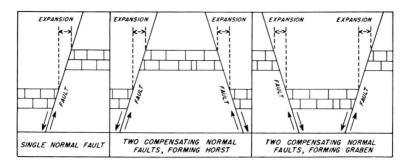

FIGURE 5 - 3

Illustrating diagrammatically the expansion of the Earth's surface due to normal faulting.

compressive stresses, which would have to be prevalent if the Earth were shrinking in volume and its surface decreasing in area. Not only do normal faults, therefore, fail to support the theory that the Earth is shrinking in volume, but, on the contrary, they point strongly towards the opposite theory that the Earth is expanding in volume. The rupture in the Earth's Crust, constituting a normal fault, does not persist indefinitely in length, but always terminates in both directions, usually by gradual decrease in the amount of displacement along the fault plane until the walls come together and the break ceases. Sometimes a normal fault passes at each end into a monoclinal fold, which in turn dies out gradually. A normal fault dies out in depth also.

Reverse or thrust faults are divisible into two kinds: steeply dipping faults, which are usually termed reverse faults; and flatly dipping faults, which are commonly called thrust faults. It would

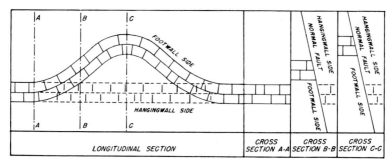

FIGURE 5 - 4

Illustrating diagrammatically the termination of a normal fault horizontally in both directions,—the vertical displacement being greatly exaggerated.

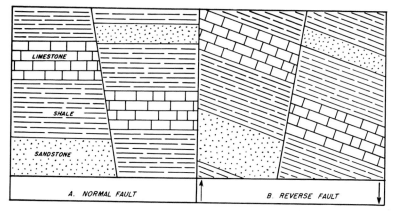

FIGURE 5 - 5

Illustrating diagrammatically the conversion of a normal fault (A) into a reverse fault (B), through tilting of the block in which the fault occurs.

require so large a compressive stress to form a reverse fault, that probably most faults of this nature are formed in some other manner. Thus it may be a normal fault, which, through subsequent tilting of the block of the Earth's Crust, in which it is situated, has now acquired the attitude of a reverse fault, as per Figure 5 - 5; or it may actually be a transcurrent fault, since a transcurrent fault may appear in cross-section to be either a normal or a reverse fault, according to the relative positions of the formations in its two walls, as per Figure 5 - 6. In either case, a reverse fault offers no evidence

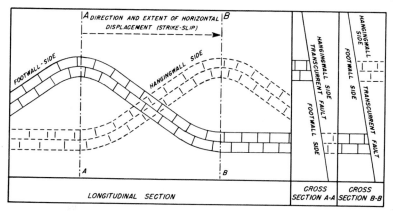

FIGURE 5 - 6

Illustrating diagrammatically seemingly normal movement (Cross-section A-A) and reverse movement (Cross-section B-B) at different places along a transcurrent fault.

one way or the other as to the possible shrinkage or expansion of
the Earth in volume. A thrust fault, consisting of a flatly dipping
fault with its hangingwall overriding its footwall, on the other hand,
results in an apparent shortening of the Earth's Crust, and therefore
seems to contradict the evidence of normal faults; but it will be
shown that this contradiction is only apparent and not real. Unlike
normal faults, thrust faults are relatively few in number and very
erratic in their distribution,—many large areas of the Earth's surface
containing none. All thrust faults occur in proximity to outcrops
of intrusive igneous masses, or where there is reason to believe that
such igneous masses, although not exposed on the surface, exist at

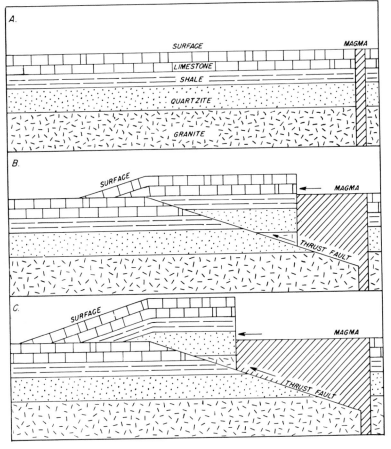

FIGURE 5 - 7

Illustrating diagrammatically the mode of formation of a thrust fault, in three
successive stages,—disregarding erosion.

relatively shallow depth; and this relationship is significant of the genetic bond between the two, for thrust faults are formed by local igneous intrusions in the Earth's Crust, resulting in the displacement of portions of the upper part of the Crust. Such an intrusion probably begins with the formation of a dike, as per Figure 5 - 7; then the dike expands laterally near the surface, where the Crust can give way and make room for this expansion, which usually takes place only on one side of the dike, where the Crust happens to be weakest. The part of the Crust displaced by the expansion of the dike is wedge-shaped in longitudinal section,—the thin edge of the wedge, which is also the free edge and is the part most distant from the dike, being shoved forward and overriding the surface in front of it like a glacier, although erosion may remove the front edge nearly as fast as it advances. The displaced block in its simplest form is U-shaped,—less commonly V-shaped,—in cross-section, and consists of a flatly dipping bottom, called the "sole-plane," and two steeply dipping walls, called "tear faults," which move in a direction parallel to the sole-plane, and are actually transcurrent faults somewhat obliquely inclined. Unlike the case of a normal fault, a thrust fault block is completely detached from the surrounding formations, and moves forward and obliquely upward, somewhat like a bureau drawer, if the latter were tilted somewhat upward and were pushed from behind instead of being pulled from in front. Sometimes the lateral expansion of the dike takes place in stages, separated by intervals of repose, and in that case a complex thrust fault may be formed, consisting of two or more parallel thrust faults, superposed one above the other,—the movement along them taking place at separate times. Sometimes, too, the igneous dike, which furnishes the motive power, extends itself longitudinally as well as expanding sidewise, and then as fast as the longitudinal extension progresses, new thrust fault blocks are shoved forward, parallel to and alongside the previously formed blocks, creating a compound thrust fault, consisting of a series of adjacent thrust fault blocks, separated from one another by tear faults, so that the relationship of the individual thrust fault blocks to each other is somewhat like that of the keys of a piano. The effect is to produce an apparently

FOOTNOTE: For simplicity of illustration, Figures 5 - 7 and 5 - 9 show the body of magma, which supplies the motive power, as extending to and exposed at the Earth's surface, but actually this never happens, because the magma body is always capped, either by a section of the crust, or by a blanket of volcanic products,—lava flows and beds of fragmental material (See p. 167).

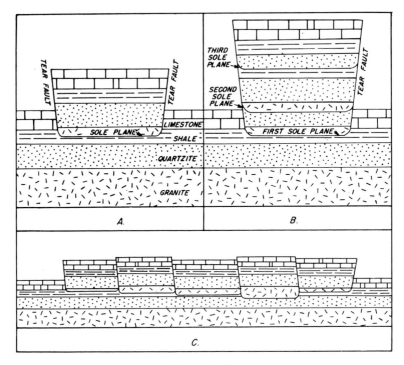

FIGURE 5 - 8

Illustrating diagrammatically:

    A. A cross-section of a simple thrust fault block.

    B. A cross-section of a complex thrust fault block.

    C. A cross-section of a compound thrust fault block.

       disregarding erosion, in each instance.

wide thrust fault plane, whose subdivision by tear faults into separate smaller thrust fault blocks may not be very obvious. A wedge
snowplow pushed forward by a locomotive through deep snow sometimes shoves the snow aside in successive blocks along an upward
inclined plane formed in the snow, in a manner very much like the
action described in the formation of a compound thrust fault. Superficially a thrust fault gives the appearance of shortening the Earth's
surface, but, viewing a longitudinal section along a thrust fault, it
will be noted that only the overriding block has moved, to an extent
just sufficient to accommodate the expansion of the igneous dike, and
that the Earth's Crust beneath remains undisturbed, so that no
actual shortening of the Earth's perimeter has taken place.

Transcurrent faults, having a generally horizontal direction of movement, tend neither to decrease nor increase the Earth's surface area, which would accompany a decrease or increase in its volume. Most transcurrent faults are probably tear faults, which are portions of thrust faults, but some transcurrent faults appear to have been formed through the drag action of igneous sills, advancing through the Earth's Crust at depth, although the mechanics of deep-seated Earth movements are rather obscure and complicated. In conclusion, it may now be said, by way of summary, that normal faults tend to bring about an increase in the surface area of the Earth, indicative of an expansion of its volume, and the great number of normal faults suggests that the total effect may be considerable. Thrust faults and transcurrent faults, however, are due to other causes, and have no effect in this direction, one way or the other.

It is now in order to consider the features of folding in the Earth's Crust,—a phenomenon, which in the past has been believed to provide almost irrefutable evidence of a contraction of the Earth's surface area, due to shrinkage of its volume. However, if the latter were the cause, it would be reasonable to expect folding to be distributed over the face of the Earth with some approach to uniformity, —that is to say, the folds should be distributed with fair regularity, should occur at moderately frequent intervals, and should pursue random courses, ranging from northerly-southerly to easterly-westerly, with no particular preference for any one direction. The fold pattern of the Earth's surface, however, does not satisfy these conditions, for the folds are concentrated almost wholly in certain tracts and are absent over large areas, while in any tract, where they occur, they commonly exhibit a conspicuous parallellism. Thus in the central part of the North American continent there are two major areas of post-Proterozoic buckling,—the Appalachian tract and the Rocky Mountain-Cordilleran tract, which are separated from each other by the Mississippi Valley, a tract over 2,000 miles in width,— nearly 1/10th of the Earth's circumference,—in which there are only shallow undulations with a few low domical elevations, quite different in aspect from the two mountainous tracts, which border it. In the latter, furthermore, the folds, instead of having random directions, are notably parallel, and are of dominantly northerly-southerly trend. In other continents comparable situations prevail,— the folding being concentrated within certain limited tracts, in each of which more or less parallelism of the folds is evident, while over adjacent broad areas there has been practically no contemporaneous folding. It appears, therefore, that the crumpling of the Earth's Crust is greatly localized, so that, if it is to be attributed to shrinkage of the Earth's interior, it is necessary to assume, either that the shrinkage of the subjacent interior is similarly localized, or else that certain segments of the Earth's Crust possess sufficient strength to resist the tendency to buckle, and, instead, transmit their share of the compressive stress by lateral thrust to adjacent weaker segments. There is no evidence to support the possibility of materially different degrees of contractibility of the interior beneath different areas, for variations in the chemical composition of the Earth's Crust could not be sufficient to occasion any material difference in the coefficients of expansion. As to the alternative explanation, the thickness of the Earth's Crust is estimated at about 30 miles, on the average, which, for a segment like the Mississippi Valley, some 2,000 miles across, would amount to only 1.5% of its surface diameter; and it would obviously exceed the strength of such a relatively thin crustal segment to withstand a tremendous shear between its base and the interior and to transmit a thrust sufficient to cause folding of the adjacent Appalachian and Rocky Mountain folded tracts. Moreover, it can be shown that the forces causing the folding of these two tracts did not come from the direction of the Mississippi Valley, but, on the contrary, from the opposite directions.

The assumption, therefore, that folding of the Earth's Crust, where it occurs, is due to shrinkage of its interior does not stand up under investigation. Instead, the fact that all folded tracts occur in proximity to the outcrops of intrusive igneous masses, or where there is reason to believe that such igneous masses, although not exposed on the surface, underlie the folded areas at relatively shallow depth, is significant, and indicates that, like thrust faults, folds are formed by local igneous intrusion in the Earth's Crust, resulting in local compression and folding of the immediately adjacent portions of the Crust. The mechanics of such action are identical with those which create thrust faults; in fact, folding and thrust faulting commonly occur together, generated by the same cause. Thrust faults seem more likely to form in relatively strong, massive, homogenous formations, and folding in relatively weak, bedded, heterogenous formations. As in the case of thrust faulting, the intrusion, which causes folding, probably begins with the formation of a dike; then the dike expands laterally near the surface, where the Crust can give way and make room for this expansion, which usually takes place only on one side of the dike, in the direction where the Crust

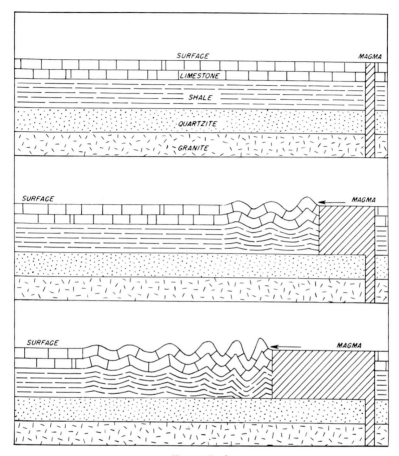

FIGURE 5 - 9

Illustrating diagrammatically the mode of formation of folds, in three successive stages,—disregarding erosion.

is weakest; and as the expansion of the dike, due to feeding of further magma from below, progresses, the intruded formations on its expanding side are crumpled into folds through the compressive stress created by the expansion. The folding does not extend relatively far below the surface, for at depth a different effect, later described, is produced. The contraction in surface area, due to folding, exactly equals the increase due to the expansion of the dike, so that the net result is no change at all. It is concluded, therefore, that folding of the Earth's surface indicates neither a decrease or expansion of this surface, but that, like thrust faulting, it is due to local adjustment consequent upon igneous intrusion. An excellent illustration of the relationship between igneous intrusion and surface folding and thrust faulting, as exposed by later erosion, is furnished on a large scale by the Appalachian Mountains, in eastern United States, which consist of a large intrusive body of granite, trending north-northeasterly for a distance of about a thousand miles, flanked on its western side by a broad belt of folded and thrust faulted sedimentary formations, but lacking any similar belt on its eastern side. Evidently the pressure exerted by this granitic intrusion has been directed westerly.

The strongest and most conclusive evidence as to whether the Earth is shrinking in volume is afforded by igneous intrusions into the Crust and by extrusions upon its surface. From the earliest geological periods, of which there is visible record on the Earth's surface, down to the present day, there have been numerous recurrent outpourings of lava and expulsions of fragmental volcanic material on an impressive scale on the Earth's surface, while much vaster intrusive masses have penetrated into and occupied large volumes of the Earth's Crust. There is evidently some potent propulsive agency responsible for the ascent of magmatic masses, contrary to the influence of gravity, and against the tremendous resistance of the massive rock formations of the Earth's Crust.

The theory of a shrinking interior affords no satisfactory explanation of this phenomenon, because, according to it, the reverse effect should be produced. The existence of an over-large Crust draped loosely about a shrinking interior should afford ample room for the containment of any igneous magma, and there should be no necessity for its ascent into and through the Crust. The reason most commonly advanced for volcanic phenomena, under this theory, is that the upward progress of magmatic masses is local only, and is brought about as incidental to the adjustment of isostatic equilibrium in different parts of the Earth's Crust. The removal, by erosion, of material from land surfaces and its deposition in the sea, thereby increasing the load on ocean basins and lessening it on continental areas is compensated, according to the isostatic hypothesis, by the slow flow of plastic material at great depths below the surface, from beneath the oceanic subsiding areas to beneath the continental rising areas; and it is held that, as incidental to this slow subterranean transfer of material, the upward pressure beneath the rising areas, transmitted laterally from beneath the sinking areas, results in the forcing of abyssal material upwards into and through the Crust in places. This hypothesis, while plausible in some respects, fails to explain satisfactorily the lack of relationship between the areas of large oceanic sedimentation, which are chiefly off-shore and at the mouths of large rivers, and the positions of the eruptive provinces. Thus, if sedimentation along continental margins was the sole or at least the most potent cause of isostatic adjustment of equilibrium in the Earth's Crust, effected by sub-crustal creep of magma in the form of a plastic solid, each continent should be ringed, adjacent to the ocean basins, with rising mountain masses and with concordant volcanic activity; but such is very far from being the case. Thus, on the North and South American continents, the amount of sediment carried by rivers and discharged into the Atlantic Ocean greatly exceeds that similarly deposited in the Pacific Ocean; yet it is along the western shoreline of these continents that mountain making forces have been most active, and that igneous activity has been most manifest, in recent geological times. Despite the vast weight of sand and mud annually deposited in the Gulf of Mexico by the Mississippi River, there is no evidence that it is producing any local effect on the sub-crustal interior of the Earth in that area. The existence of mid-oceanic volcanic islands, such as Easter and the Fiji Islands in the Pacific Ocean and Ascension and St. Helena Islands in the Atlantic Ocean, far from sources of sedimentation, does not harmonize with the isostatic hypothesis. In some places on the Earth's surface coast lines are rising, as shown by elevated wave-cut terraces, while elsewhere they are sinking, as indicated by drowned river valleys, but nowhere is there any consistent relationship or unmistakable connection between these manifestations on the one hand, and erosion, sedimentation and eruptive activity on the other. If isostasy has any effect on the elevation and subsidence of the Earth's Crust in different places, it must be relatively small. Representing a seesaw balance between erosion and sedimentation, it should, if it were the only cause of crustal movement, have long ago run down, like any other seesaw, because of the retarding effect of friction caused by the resistance of the Earth's Crust to displacement.

Another theory, which has been advanced, to account for igneous intrusions and volcanic eruptions, is the levitative or buoyant effect of gases entrapped in magmas. This buoyant effect exists, but it is insufficient to account for the pressure manifested, by means of which magmas force their way upwards through unfissured formations, against the tremendous weight and resistance of the formations above them. Only when magma is ascending in some open channel, like a volcanic vent, does the levitative effect of the contained gases become operative, as later shown, and then only in the upper part of the vent to any considerable extent.

The most convincing evidence of the existence of magmatic pressure, much greater than can be accounted for by isostasy or by the levitative effect of entrapped gases, is supplied by certain igneous phenomena. Thus, where magma, in the flat shape of a sill or the domical shape of a laccolith, is being intruded along a nearly horizontal plane in rock formations, it must be exerting sufficient pressure to lift the superincumbent formations bodily; and where, as in many known instances, the thickness of the formations thus lifted has been a mile or more, the pressure exerted by the magma

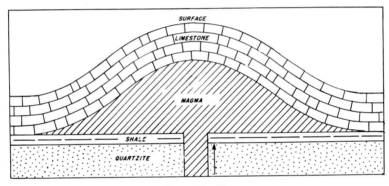

FIGURE 5 - 10

Illustrating diagrammatically the lifting of a section of the Earth's Crust, in the formation of a laccolith.

in lifting this dead weight must amount to three tons per square inch of horizontal surface or more.

Many intrusive masses, at depths too great to displace portions of the crust by folding or thrust faulting, make room for their own expansion by squeezing the intruded formations, creating in them a schistose or gneissic structure; and in some such instances a reduction of one fourth to one half of the volume of the intruded rocks, for short distances away from the intrusive, is indicated by the crumpling of small veins or dikes along the direction of pressure. The force necessary to accomplish such a result is probably comparable to the dead weight of a section of the Crust, which, under static conditions, could bring about similar effects, and, where the

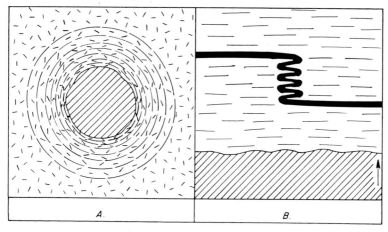

FIGURE 5 - 11

Illustrating diagrammatically:

A. The formation of a zone of compression gneiss around an intrusive stock in the Earth's Crust.

B. The compression of intruded formations, indicated by the crumpling of an originally straight dike. (After Josiah E. Spurr, *"The Ore Magmas,"* Vol I, p. 168, Copyright, McGraw-Hill Book Company, Inc., 1923)

thickness of such a section of Crust was three miles, the pressure exerted would amount to nine tons per square inch of surface.

In many volcanoes, lava is discharged from the crater at considerable heights above the surrounding country, and hence the pressure necessary to elevate a column of lava to such a height can be calculated. One of the most impressive examples is furnished by the volcano of Mauna Loa in the Hawaiian Islands. Not only does it rise more than 13,000 ft. above the surrounding ocean, but its base lies some 15,000 ft. below the surface of the sea, so that the total height of the volcano above its base is some 28,000 ft. Calculating the weight of a lava column of this height, after allowing for the partially compensating pressure of the ocean on the base, indicates

FOOTNOTE: One of the earliest and most convincing descriptions of the effects of the tremendous force exerted by igneous magmas in emplacing themselves in the Earth's Crust, as evidenced by doming, folding, faulting, and the development of schistose and gneissoid structure in the invaded formations, was written thirty years ago by the eminent geologist, the late Josiah E. Spurr, who referred to this magmatic force as "telluric pressure," but mistakenly attributed it to the expansive power of magmatic gases. *"The Ore Magmas,"* Vol. I, pp. 157-252. Copyright, 1923, McGraw-Hill Book Co., Inc., New York, N. Y.

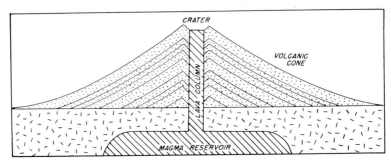

FIGURE 5 - 12

Illustrating diagrammatically the ascent of lava in the throat of a volcano, due to pressure exerted on the magma reservoir at its base, by expansion of the Earth's interior.

that it would require a pressure of about twelve tons per square inch at the base of the lava column to elevate it up to the crater.

The only possible explanation of such igneous phenomena is that the interior of the Earth, underlying the Crust, is expanding in volume; for such an expanding interior, confined within a rigid and inelastic Crust, could obtain relief only by forcibly penetrating into the Crust, displacing or elevating portions of it in the process, and breaking completely through it in places to expel some of the surplus bulk on its surface. A review of all the available evidence, therefore, not only fails completely to support the hypothesis that the interior of the Earth is shrinking in volume, but, on the contrary, tends to establish the opposite theory that the interior of the Earth is expanding in volume.

The explanation of this latter phenomenon is suggested by the well established fact that certain unstable, relatively heavy, radioactive elements, such as uranium and thorium, present in minerals in the Earth's body, are disintegrating into stable, relatively light, nonradioactive elements, which are among those constituting the minerals that compose the bulk of the Earth's body at the present time. Thus one atom of uranium^{238}, when completely disintegrated, creates one atom of lead^{206} and eight atoms of helium^{4}; while one atom of thorium^{232}, when completely disintegrated, creates one atom of lead^{208} and six atoms of helium^{4}. Since the atoms of all these elements are very nearly the same size, the result in the case of uranium would be that its end products would have a volume about nine times as great as the original atom of uranium, while, in the case of thorium, its end products would have a volume about seven

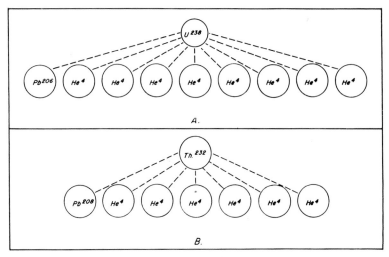

FIGURE 5 - 13

Illustrating diagrammatically the increase in volume resulting from the complete disintegration of an atom of uranium[238] and an atom of thorium[232].

times as great as the original atom of thorium,—provided, in each instance, all were in the solid state. Helium, however, is a gas at normal temperatures and pressures, occupying a volume, at 0° C. and 760 mm. pressure, about 1120 times as great as if it were a solid. Hence, at the Earth's surface, the volume expansion of uranium into its end products would be about 1 to 996, while the similar volume expansion of thorium into its end products would be about 1 to 960. Within the Earth's Crust, of course, the superincumbent rock pressure at any certain level would correspondingly reduce the volume of gaseous helium, until at a depth of about 20,000 ft. below the surface gaseous helium would be compressed into a volume corresponding to that of solid helium. The disintegration of uranium, thorium, and other known radioactive elements in the Earth's body into simpler and lighter elements, therefore, could supply a cause for expansion of the Earth's body and increase in its surface area, but it is doubtful whether their contribution to this effect would be very substantial, and still more doubtful whether they could be responsible for vulcanism and for orogeny (non-volcanic mountain building), since uranium, thorium and other known terrestrial radioactive elements appear to be confined almost wholly,—or at least in much the largest concentration,—to the Earth's Crust, while the ultimate source of vulcanism and orogeny seems to lie below the

Crust, somewhere in the interior. The evidence on which this conclusion is based is that present vulcanism and orogeny are confined to certain small areas, which are scattered very irregularly over the Earth's surface, whereas uranium, thorium, etc., seem to be distributed throughout the Crust with a fair degree of uniformity; that ultrabasic rocks, whose normal locality is below the Crust, have in places been forced upwards into it; and that earthquakes, which are phenomena directly connected with vulcanism and orogeny, are in many instances generated some distance below the bottom of the Crust.

It is true that the ultimate cause of vulcanism and orogeny, with the concomitant expansion of the Earth's body, can most logically be explained by the disintegration of unstable, relatively heavy and compact, radioactive atoms into stable, relatively light atoms, with consequent expansion of volume, but such atoms would have to differ from those known to exist within the Crust, through having far greater weight, complexity and instability, and they would have to be concentrated at the Earth's center. The reason why such atoms could not be distributed somewhat uniformly through the Earth's interior, below the Crust, is that in such case the expansion of the overlying surface should also be somewhat uniform and the distribution of volcanic and orogenic effects over the surface should be somewhat regular. As a matter of fact, however, vulcanism and orogeny are at present concentrated within certain isolated areas, which are erratically distributed over the face of the Earth, and which cover altogether probably less than 1/100th of 1% of the Earth's surface; and it is in these relatively small and isolated volcanic and orogenic areas that the Earth's expansion in volume is most obviously and conspicuously taking place. The remainder of the Earth's surface is quiescent, and is expanding but slightly if at all. This erratic distribution of vulcanism and orogeny seems to have prevailed throughout all geological epochs, except that the location of the active volcanic and orogenic areas has shifted from place to place at different times. Such an erratic distribution of the volcanic and orogenic areas, if due to atomic disintegration within the Earth's body, could have resulted only if the expanding mass were situated at the Earth's center, since an expansion there would not tend to lift all the superjacent body of the Earth uniformly, but would seek relief in those areas, where the weight happened at that time to be least, somewhat as steam, generated at the bottom of a tea-kettle, does not rise uniformly through the overlying water in the form of minute bubbles, but collects in large bubbles which pursue selected paths upwards.

The preceding conclusions all harmonize with the assumption, set forth in the preceding chapter, that the center of the Earth is occupied by a Nucleus of high density atoms, inherited from the Sun and, through it, from the Primordial Mass. This high density Nucelus is assumed to be intensely radioactive on its periphery, where it is disintegrating into stable, lighter atoms, similar to those constituting the body of the Earth, which in fact are only earlier formed disintegration products of the same Nucleus. The disintegration of the high density atoms constituting the Nucleus would take place in stages, so that between the Nucleus and the Earth's Core there would be a zone of uncertain width, consisting of intermediate disintegration products. The density of the Nucleus is not definitely known, and hence the ratio of expansion caused by its disintegration cannot be determined; but if, for purposes of illustration, the specific gravity of the Nucleus is assumed to be 60,000 and that of the disintegration products immediately surrounding the transition zone is assumed to be about 10, which is the approximate specific gravity of the contiguous part of the Earth's Core, due to pressure, then the ratio of expansion would be 1 to 6,000,—that is to say, for each cubic foot of Nucleus disintegrated, 6,000 cubic feet of disintegration products would be formed. Expansion would also take place concurrently at higher levels in the Earth's body, in consequence of this central expansion, so that the total eventual ratio of expansion might be of the order of 1 to 15,000 or even higher; but the details, together with the effects of this expansion, will be discussed in the succeeding chapter.

CHAPTER SIX

The Phenomena of Vulcanism and Orogeny

The conclusion has been reached, from the evidence presented in preceding chapters, that the center of the Earth is occupied by a relatively small Nucleus of high density atoms, inherited from the Sun, and that this Nucleus is disintegrating on its periphery into lighter atoms, such as constitute the remainder of the body of the Earth, and similar to those which may be observed in the Earth's Crust. As the disintegration products of the Nucleus are formed, they would surround it, and would tend, because of the great expansion in volume accompanying their formation, to lift the entire superincumbent mass of the Earth's body, but the upward pressure thus generated would produce different effects upon the Earth's Core, its Mantle and its Crust. In the liquid Core, as in any other liquid body, the pressure would be transmitted equally throughout its mass, and in its expansion, it would tend to transmit pressure uniformly over its surface to the overlying Mantle. But the Mantle, a plastic solid, would be differently affected; for, instead of yielding uniformly to this pressure, it would tend to give way only in the areas where the resistance to this pressure, determined by the weight of overlying portions of the Earth's mass, happened to be least, resulting in the formation of a number of columnar zones, extending radially from the top of the Core to the Earth's surface, hereinafter referred to as pressure columns, as per Figure 6 - 1 A. This selective effect of upward pressure, transmitted from the surface of the Core to the bottom of the Mantle, has previously been compared to what happens in a boiling pot, where the water vapor formed along its bottom does not make its way uniformly upward through the overlying water as numerous minute bubbles, but collects into large bubbles, which choose distinct upward paths to follow. The comparison is not exact, however, because there is no actual movement of the material in a pressure column from its bottom to its top. Instead, for each pressure column, the top of the Core bulges upward for a

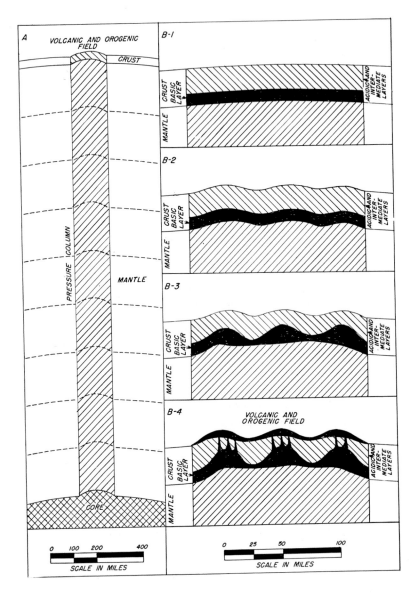

FIGURE 6 - 1

A. Illustrating diagrammatically the formation of a pressure column in the Earth's Mantle.

B-1 to B-4. Illustrating diagrammatically successive steps in the formation of a volcanic and orogenic field on the Earth's surface at the top of a pressure column.

short distance, doming each successive superjacent horizon in the
overlying Mantle within the limits of the pressure column, up to the
bottom of the Crust. The Crust, being relatively rigid and inelastic,
resists this upward pressure, until eventually compelled to yield to
a force superior in its strength, partially by doming to some extent,
but probably chiefly by the plastic rock material composing the top
of the Mantle being forced into it and possibly eventually through it
to the surface, in greater or less degree, thus creating a volcanic
and orogenic field, as illustrated in Figure 6 - 1, B - 1 to B - 4. Pressure columns may vary in size, probably from a minimum of about
twenty miles diameter to several hundred miles diameter, and they
may also vary in cross-section from circular through elliptical to
irregular. When, by such terrestrial mechanics, the weight of this
pressure column, culminating in a volcanic and orogenic field on the
surface, had eventually reached a point, through the upward bulging
of the top of the Core at the base of the Mantle, where it equalled or
exceeded that of neighboring parts of the Earth's body, thereupon
the growth of this pressure column would cease, and the volcanic
and orogenic field capping it on the surface would become extinct,
while a new pressure column, stemming from another base and sur-
facing elsewhere, would be formed, and the cycle of growth previously described would be repeated. An illustration of the selective
localization of pressure columns within the Earth's body, and of the
surface volcanic and orogenic fields, in which they terminate upward,
at different geological times, is provided in the United States, which
is divided from east to west into three physiographic zones,—the
Appalachian zone, next to the Atlantic Ocean; the Rocky Mountain-
Cordilleran zone, next to the Pacific Ocean; and the Mississippi
Valley zone, in between. In the Mississippi Valley zone, the most
recent igneous and orogenic activity on a large scale took place
during the Proterozoic era, and there has been only slight activity
there since; while in the Appalachian zone it happened chiefly during
Carboniferous and Triassic times, and the zone has been quiescent
since; and in the Rocky Mountain-Cordilleran zone it took place
principally during Jurassic, Cretaceous and Tertiary times, and has
since been declining in strength. Elsewhere over the Earth's surface
a similar concentration of igneous and orogenic activity in certain
tracts during certain geological periods of time, while other areas
were enjoying comparative repose, can be noted; but at some time
or another during the Earth's history every part of its surface seems
to have been subjected to such activity, so that no part has enjoyed

complete immunity. In fact, certain areas can be observed to have been twice visited by these stresses at widely separated intervals, during their visible geological history, and it is not improbable that the entire surface of the Earth has been thus dealt with two or even more times, since the formation of the solid Crust. While the effect of isostasy as an initial cause of vulcanism and orogenic activity has been denied, and while the equilibrium of the Earth's body is in no such delicate state of balance that relatively small transfers of material from one part of its surface to another by the forces of erosion can produce prompt and complete adjustment, as the proponents of the isostatic theory assume, it is probable that the effect of surface erosion in lightening the weight of some segments of the Earth's body and increasing the weight of other segments is eventually contributory to the localization of pressure columns.

While the effect of the disintegration of complex, high density atoms, constituting the Earth's Nucleus, into lighter and simpler atoms is doubtless the largest single factor in the expansion of the Earth in volume, it is not the only one; because, as each successive horizon of the Earth's body is domed upward, within the limits of a pressure column, it invades a zone of less pressure overlying it, and hence tends to expand in volume; and the cumulative effect of such expansion, plus the dilating effect of magmatic gases in molten magma, upon solidification within depths of less than 20,000 ft. below the surface of the Earth's Crust, must be considerable, although impossible of computation. The total expansion of the Earth in volume during geologically historic times, since the commencement of the Archeozoic era, can only be guessed at, but the Earth's radius may have been increased some five miles during this period, which would indicate an expansion of about 4/10th of 1% in volume, while the total expansion since the formation of a solid Crust has probably been many times as much. It is certain, at least, that any remnant of the original crustal surface, if still surviving, must be deeply buried beneath subsequent surface accumulations, because the oldest formations now visible consist of ancient sediments,—shales and sandstones,—together with lava flows and fragmental volcanic material, all greatly metamorphosed, and usually complexly intruded by igneous masses.

Before discussing the effect of pressure columns on the Earth's Crust, it may be well to review the nature and composition of the Crust. During the period when the Earth was molten, there was a tendency toward gravitative segregation of the constituents of the magma according to weight,—the lighter accumulating near the surface and the heavier with depth, so that ultimately there was formed, as the body of the Earth congealed, a top zone of acidic composition forming granite, etc., upon solidification; a zone of intermediate composition forming diorite, etc., next below; a zone of basic composition forming diabase, etc., next below; while ultrabasic material, such as peridotite, including a small proportion of nickel-iron, which increased slowly with depth down to a certain level, constituted the remainder of the body of the Earth above the Nucleus. The zones would not be sharply defined, but would grade into each other. The thickness of the various zones can only be guessed; but, for purposes of discussion, it may be assumed that the acidic, intermediate and basic zones were each about ten miles in thickness, and together formed the Crust of the Earth, while ultrabasic material, in the form of a plastic solid, constituted the top of the immediately underlying Mantle.

The evolution of a pressure column within the Earth's Crust takes place in two stages: (1) the intrusive stage; and   (2) the extrusive or volcanic stage. The two stages merge into one another, but the intrusive stage, of course, must commence before the volcanic stage does, and may continue for some time after the latter has started. In some instances, where the pressure column is small in cross-section, only the intrusive stage may occur and the volcanic stage may never develop.

During the intrusive stage, masses of rock in the form of plastic solids from the top of the Mantle, or of rock in the lower part of the Crust, originally in the form of rigid solids, but converted by subjacent pressure into plastic solids, move upward through the Crust at different places, within the limits of pressure columns, utilizing localities of relative weakness for their ascent, and this process continues upward as each successive overlying horizon is subjected to pressure from that immediately underlying it. Two important processes, in addition to forcible penetration upward, are operative at this time: (1) palingenesis; and   (2) assimilation.

As pressure tends to raise the melting point of rocks, so reduction of pressure tends to lower it; and hence many rock masses, which are solid at the depth at which they lie within the Earth's Crust, become liquid, at the same temperature, at shallower depths or at the surface. Consequently, rock masses in the state of plastic solids, as they are being forced upward by deep-seated pressure into or through the Earth's Crust, eventually attain levels where, at their original temperature or nearly so, they become transformed into viscous liquids, called magmas. Magmas thus formed are purely local in their occurrence, and are confined to certain levels, determined by the temperature, within pressure columns in the Earth's Crust. In this form of a viscous liquid or magma, upward migrating rock masses in the Earth's Crust possess much greater mobility and penetrative power than they previously had as a plastic solid, and hence their ascent toward the surface is greatly facilitated and their rate of progress accelerated. Lavas usually attain the surface at temperatures ranging from about 1,000° C. to 1,200° C., but underground the magmas, from which they originate, may be fluid at lower temperatures, down to about 600° C., because of their content of gases, which lowers the melting point.

Sometimes some of the gases present in a magma migrate upward into the solid formation constituting the roof of the magma chamber. The latter term designates the space occupied by the magma, which, however, was never a void, but was created by the magma and filled by it as fast as formed. These upward migrating gases, because of their heat but more particularly because of their chemical activity, sometimes cause part of the roof rock of the magma chamber to melt, thus creating additional masses of liquid rock or magma, which, upon solidifying, will do so as an igneous rock, often quite different in aspect and nature from the form originally possessed, which may have been that of a sedimentary or metamorphic rock formation. This process of melting in place and again congealing into a solid, whether in the same place or after having migrated elsewhere, is called palingenesis, or sometimes granitization.

A very potent method of advance upward and laterally for the magmas in the Earth's Crust is provided by the process of assimilation, whereby some of the solid rock adjoining the magma chamber on the sides and top is liquefied and incorporated into their substance. Assimilation, which is a process of chemical dissolution, rather than melting, and which depends for its effectiveness largely upon the gas content of the magma, is most pronounced at the roof of the magma chamber, where, by the method of "magmatic stoping," tongues of magma insinuate themselves along joints, cracks, fissures or other lines of weakness in the roof rocks, gradually prying loose blocks of these rocks (xenoliths), which sink into and are engulfed in the magma, and thus being open to attack on all sides, are eventually digested, assimilated and mixed with the magma. By this assimilation process, the chemical character of a body of

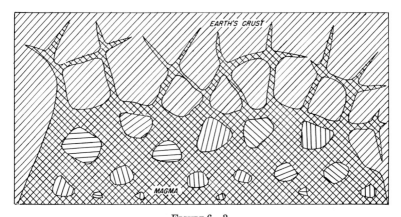

FIGURE 6 - 2

Illustrating diagrammatically the process of "magmatic stoping" in the Earth's Crust.

magma, or that part of it engaged in assimilating its walls and roof, will be more or less changed from its original composition, depending upon the nature and amount of the material absorbed. Thus limestone and dolomite, which have been assimilated, will contribute lime and magnesia, together with carbon dioxide gas; sandstone and quartzite will supply silica; shale and slate will add silica, alumina, iron, lime, potash and soda; while igneous rocks will contribute different constituents in varying amount. Basic magmas are particularly effective in assimilating silicious rocks, whether of igneous or sedimentary origin, which they may adjoin. By the process of assimilation a great variety of less common igneous rocks has been produced from the more abundant types.

It has been claimed, however, that not assimilation but differentiation should be credited with the formation of most of the different types of igneous rocks. Differentiation is a process, whereby a magma tends to separate into two or more independent rock types of more or less dissimilar character. It is illustrated on a small scale in the crystallization of a holocrystalline, or completely crystalline, igneous rock, such as granite, from its magma, whereby, through molecular attraction, similar molecules, such as those of quartz, feldspar, mica, etc., tend, during crystallization from the cooling magmatic mass, to assemble together to form crystals of such molecules. But molecular attraction in a magma is a relatively weak force, capable of exerting influence only over small distances, for which reason similar crystals in a holocrystalline igneous rock are rarely separated by more than a fraction of an inch. Molecular attraction, therefore, is not a force which can be effective in promoting large scale differentiation of an igneous mass; and the latter can be accomplished only in two ways: (1) by gravitative separation; and (2) by fractional crystallization.

Gravitative separation is a process whereby, of solid particles suspended in a liquid, the heavier tend to sink through it the faster, so that eventually the upper part of the liquid tends to contain more of the lighter particles and the lower part more of the heavier particles. The more viscous the liquid and the smaller the particles, the less would be the tendency for such separation, because a viscous liquid offers more resistance than a thinner liquid to the sinking of a solid particle through it, while, since the surface of a particle varies as the square of its diameter and its mass varies as its cube, the smaller the particle the more resistance it offers to the effect of gravity in an enclosing liquid, until eventually very minute particles of even heavy metals, such as gold, will float in water. Magmas are very viscous liquids, especially under the heavy pressure to which they are subjected underground, and it is doubtful whether any of the constituents of igneous rocks, when crystallizing out from the magma, possess sufficient mass to be able to overcome the viscosity of the magma and to sink down through it. Certainly there is no evidence of any difference in composition, such as might be caused by differentiation, between the tops and the lowermost exposures of large granitic masses, revealed by erosion over a large vertical range, as illustrated by the steep western scarp of the Sierra Nevada range in California, some 10,000 ft. in height, where it fronts the Owens River Valley. The only instances where differentiation is suggested by the evidence occurs in certain thick basic sills. This is illustrated by one of the "Purcell" sills, in British Columbia, Canada, which consists of hornblende gabbro, that has been intruded into a sedimentary series of quartzites and argillites. This sill is overlain, from the top downward, successively by biotite granite, hornblende granite, and a rock intermediate in character between the latter and the underlying gabbro, as shown in the accompanying diagrammatic section (Figure 6 - 3). This condition, however, could just as well have been produced by palingenesis, whereby the silicious sedimentary formations overlying the basic sill were penetrated for a certain distance upward by gases escaping from the sill, causing the melting of such formations, accompanied by some mixing of the silicious magma thus produced with the basic magma of the sill along their common boundary. The fact that this is what

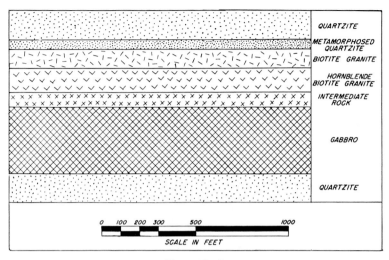

QUARTZITE

METAMORPHOSED
QUARTZITE

BIOTITE GRANITE

HORNBLENDE
BIOTITE GRANITE

INTERMEDIATE
ROCK

GABBRO

QUARTZITE

0   100 200 300   500   1000

SCALE IN FEET

FIGURE 6 - 3

Illustrating diagrammatically the effect of palingenesis in a Purcell sill, British
Columbia, Canada. (After R. A. Daly, *"Igneous Rocks and Their Origin,"* p. 344.
Copyright, 1914, McGraw-Hill Book Company, Inc., New York, N. Y.)

actually happened, rather than differentiation, is suggested by the
circumstance that, immediately overlying the top biotite granite,
there is an intensely metamorphosed quartzite horizon, recognizable
by the preservation of its bedding, which evidently represents an
intermediate stage in the process of palingenesis, not yet advanced
to the point of actual liquefaction and mixing, such as overtook the
sedimentary beds originally lying between it and the sill.

Another suggested mode of differentiation is by fractional
crystallization. The congelation of a magma does not take place
uniformly throughout its mass, but in stages, with the more insoluble
minerals crystallizing first, so that there is a certain stage in the
process when certain constituents of the magma have solidified,
while the remainder are still in liquid form. It has been suggested
that, in this condition, the still liquid portions of the magma may
be squeezed out and enter into the surrounding formations as separate intrusive bodies. The example most frequently cited in this
connection is that of pegmatite dikes, which are common around the
peripheries of some large granitic masses. The objection to this
hypothesis is that all portions of a magma, solid as well as liquid, are
under the same pressure, to which they offer the same resistance,
so that the assumption of a greater resistance by the solid portions

than by the liquid portions, as would be required to explain the proposed phenomenon, is not valid. So far as pegmatite dikes are concerned, these penetrate the outer parts of the granite mass as well as the surrounding intruded rocks, so that they could not have been formed until at least all of the outer parts of the mass had been completely solidified. Furthermore, evidence is available that pegmatite dikes are formed by palingenesis, thus withdrawing support as an example of fractional crystallization. Differentiation, as explaining the mode of formation of certain types of igneous rocks, whether by gravitative separation or by fractional crystallization, is not sufficiently proven, therefore, to justify its acceptance concurrently with the theories of palingenesis and assimilation, both of which latter are well supported by field evidence.

Magmatic masses may ascend through the Earth's Crust in three ways: (1) by thrusting aside the invaded formations; (2) by lifting them; and (3) by assimilating them. In thrusting aside the invaded formations, the squeezing to which the latter are subjected by the pressure of the magma tends to develop schistose and gneissic structure in them. So some degree this magmatic pressure can be absorbed by compression of the invaded formations into smaller volume; but this is possible only to a limited extent, and any further pressure must result in forced migration of the invaded formations elsewhere. Lateral resistance to pressure eventually builds up to an extent greater than the magma is capable of overcoming, and in that case the only direction of yielding is towards the surface, where the maximum resistance is only the dead weight of the superincumbent formations. This upward pressure, therefore, tends to dome the overlying formations above the magma to a greater or less extent. Assimilation is the simplest method, requiring no exertion of force, since the upward movement of the magma by assimilation of its roof rock closely corresponds to the decrease in volume of the roof rock due to assimilation.

The largest intrusive bodies, some of which have been exposed over areas of hundreds of square miles by subsequent erosion, are called batholiths. Batholiths have no floors, but merge in depth with the primary formations of the Earth's Crust, from which they originated. Except where subsequently bevelled by erosion, the tops of batholiths are not plane surfaces, but are irregular in detail; and from them ascend smaller satellitic intrusive structures, such as cupolas, stocks, apophyses, chonoliths, dikes, sills and laccoliths, which intrude the superincumbent formations. Cupolas are conical or domical protuberances; stocks are vertically columnar bodies; apophyses are tentacle like projections; chonoliths are irregularly shaped intrusive masses; dikes are tabular bodies standing at an attitude of more than 45° from the horizontal; sills are recumbent tabular bodies, lying at less than 45° from the horizontal; and laccoliths are sills of plano-convex cross-section, with the convex side

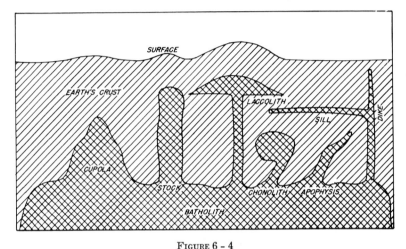

FIGURE 6 - 4

Illustrating diagrammatically different kinds of satellitic structures formed above a batholith.

uppermost. It is by means of these satellitic structures that magmas reach the surface to form volcanoes. Batholiths themselves never attain the surface, since, when they approach it closely, some satellitic structures will precede them upward, supplying conduits for the ascent of magma to form volcanoes, which will blanket the surface with their products and thus provide a protective cover. Fault fissures rarely extend below the surface of the Earth more deeply than three or four miles, and hence they afford little help to batholiths in their ascent, but such fault fissures are frequently utilized as pathways upward by the satellitic structures, which accompany batholiths. The resistance offered by the rigid rock formations of the Earth's Crust to the progress of batholiths and their satellitic structures upward and laterally cause shocks when they finally yield, and these shocks are what form the earthquakes that originate in the Earth's Crust. Earthquakes are also formed in similar fashion, but less frequently, at deeper levels within pressure columns in the Earth's Mantle.

The most common igneous rocks are the following:

Feldspars	Much (Acidic)	Quartz Little (Inter-mediate)	None (Basic)
Holocrystalline			
Dominantly ortho-clase feldspars	Granite		
Mixed feldspars	Quartz monzonite	Monzonite	
Dominantly plagio-clase feldspars	Quartz diorite	Diorite	Diabase-gabbro
Porphyritic			
Dominantly ortho-clase feldspars	Rhyolite		
Mixed feldspars	Quartz latite	Latite	
Dominantly plagio-clase feldspars	Dacite	Andesite	Basalt

The holocrystalline, or wholly crystallized, igneous rocks are con-fined wholly to intrusive bodies,—batholiths and the larger of their satellitic structures; while porphyritic, or partially crystallized, igneous rocks have their greatest development on the surface, although they also frequently constitute some of the smaller satel-litic structures. Batholiths usually range in composition from gran-itic to dioritic, which is to be expected, since magma of the former composition constitutes the top zone of the primary rock formations of the Earth's Crust, while magma of the latter composition occupies the zone next beneath. Basic batholiths, exposed by erosion on the surface, are uncommon, as is also to be expected, since they origi-nate from a still deeper level in the Earth's Crust; but, because of the relatively great mobility of basic magma, the satellitic struc-tures accompanying them are very abundant, particularly in the form of dikes and sills,—the latter often being of great thickness and wide areal extent. Ultrabasic batholiths, exposed on the sur-face, are practically non-existent, because of their still deeper source, while, for the same reason, their accompanying satellitic structures are not commonly seen.

In those instances where the satellitic structures rising from underlying and concealed batholiths chance to approach and reach the surface, volcanoes are formed. Vulcanism is so spectacular and destructive a phenomenon of nature, that it has engaged the atten-tion of mankind out of all proportion to its relative geological importance, since, of the magma which intrudes the Earth's Crust, probably less than 10% ever gains the surface. Although the satellitic structures rising from batholiths provide the means whereby the intrusive magma can attain the Earth's surface, the last stage of the ascent utilizes principally three kinds of conduits: (1) dikes; (2) collapse breccia pipes; and (3) explosion breccia pipes. The role of dikes in this connection is well known, but the function of breccia pipes is less understood and appreciated.

Collapse breccia pipes occur in rock formations of all kinds. They are probably always formed by magmatic gases escaping from underlying magma masses, and making their way upward, either along fissures or by direct penetration through the overlying rock formations. These magmatic gases, being intensely hot and chemically very active, dissolve portions of the rock formations, through which they pass, carrying them up to the surface in gaseous or liquid form; and in the voids thus created by their removal the adjacent rock caves in, and this action progresses upward as fast as room at the top is provided by continued solution of the rock by magmatic gases. Most collapse pipes, as formed, are not open, but are probably completely filled with caved rubble or breccia up to their tops, at any stage in their formation. If they eventually cave their way close to the surface, the thin section of rock formation overlying the top of the pipe often subsides into it whole, forming a cork-like capping to the pipe. However, most collapse breccia pipes probably never reach that stage in their evolution, being previously converted into explosion pipes.

Explosion pipes are breccia pipes, extending to the surface, that have been created by the explosive expansion of magmatic gases. Probably most of them originate from collapse pipes, which have approached sufficiently close to the surface, so that the magmatic gases, which they contain, provide sufficient pressure to overcome the strength of the rock formations between them and the surface, resulting in explosions, which blow holes through to the surface. Collapse and explosion pipes, when newly formed, can be distinguished from each other by the fact that an explosion pipe is surrounded by a crater-like ring of explosion debris on the surface, while a collapse pipe is marked by a subsidence pit only. Where, as in most cases, the original surface expressions of such pipes have been destroyed by subsequent erosion, the present outcrops of the two kinds of pipes are alike in consisting of more or less circular areas, occupied by breccia, more or less cemented, surrounded by solid and unshattered rock formations. In such case, they can be identified by the fact that, in a collapse pipe, the breccia fragments have all moved downward to a greater or less extent from their original positions in the rock formations, from which they have been derived; while in an explosion pipe, on the other hand, the breccia is thoroughly and chaotically mixed, regardless of its place of origin, and some of the breccia fragments occur at higher levels than their sources, showing that they have been thrown upward in the formation of the pipe.

Breccia pipes, whether of collapse or explosion origin, may occur singly, but most of them form groups, suggesting that the underlying body of magma, from which the magmatic gases that created them originated, was a near-surface intrusive structure of considerable areal extent,—probably either a sill, laccolith or broad-topped cupola. Since pipes of such nature are formed by the expansive and solvent effect of magmatic gases, escaping from underlying bodies of magma, such pipes should afford excellent opportunities

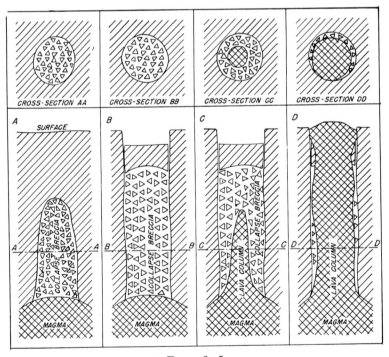

FIGURE 6 - 5

Illustrating diagrammatically the mode of formation of a volcanic vent occupying a collapse breccia pipe.

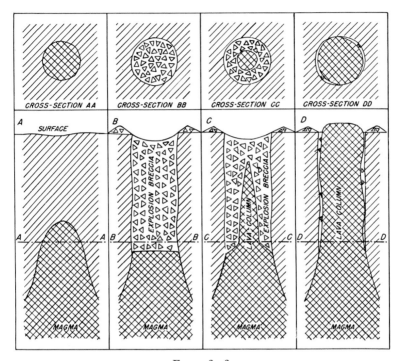

FIGURE 6 - 6

Illustrating diagrammatically the mode of formation of a volcanic vent occupying an explosion breccia pipe.

for the eventual rise of magma through them; and such is proved to be the case by field and underground exposures of many pipes, which are occupied by lava columns that have more or less completely displaced or assimilated the breccia originally filling them. The mode of formation is illustrated in Figures 6 - 5 and 6 - 6. Such lava-occupied breccia pipes are usually distributed at random, and penetrate solid rock formations,—not occurring along dikes or fissures, contrary to common belief. In many areas they are so numerous that they perforate the Earth's Crust like the holes in a colander, forming extinct volcanic fields, which constitute the surface expressions of former pressure columns in the Earth's body.

There is less variation in the composition of magma reaching the surface than there is in intrusive masses, due to the fact that in the latter the heat is better conserved and the contained gases are more readily prevented from escaping, thus promoting fluidity. Consequently, while ultra-acidic and ulta-basic intrusives are known, they have practically no surface counterparts. The chemical composition of magma, reaching the surface to form lava flows and fragmental ejecta, usually ranges from basaltic to rhyolitic, being rarely more basic than the former or more acidic than the latter. The time sequence of magma in any volcanic field usually commences with acidic or intermediate magma and ends with basic magma, although sometimes the latter is again followed, to a small extent, by acidic or intermediate magma. This sequence is due to the fact that, of the three zones constituting the Earth's Crust, the acidic zone is uppermost, the intermediate zone next, and the basic zone the lowest. Consequently when any area of the Earth's Crust is subjected to pressure from below by a pressure column, acidic magma tends to reach the surface first, forming rhyolitic volcanoes; intermediate magma next, forming andesitic volcanoes; and basic magmas last, forming basaltic volcanoes. The complete sequence is not always visible in a volcanic field, for one reason or another,— often because the earlier volcanic structures have been removed by erosion or buried beneath later ones; but when a complete sequence is visible, the above is the normal arrangement. In the unusual cases, where basic extrusives are followed by acidic or intermediate ones, the latter are usually small in volume and of palingenetic origin, due to the melting of rocks in the Earth's crust above local basaltic intrusives, through the agency of heat and gases contributed by the latter. Although basic extrusives are usually the last to reach the surface, because of their deeper source, they are much more abundant than acidic and intermediate extrusives, because of the fact that basic magmas remain fluid at considerably lower temperatures than acidic and intermediate magmas, and hence there is less likelihood of their conduits being blocked by surface or near-surface chilling.

Lavas are of two kinds, primary and secondary. Primary lavas are those, which derive directly from underlying batholithic masses, although always through the agency of intermediate satellitic structures such as cupolas, stocks, dikes, sills, laccoliths, etc., which extend upward between the batholithic masses and the surface. In such primary lavas, the chemical composition is the same as that of the parent batholiths, possibly modified to some extent by the assimilation of more or less wall rock on the way to the surface. Secondary lavas are formed by the process of palingenesis, whereby solid rocks in the Earth's Crust, either igneous or sedimentary, are melted in place through the agency of heat and magmatic gases, supplied by adjacent or underlying primary magma. The secondary or palingenetic magma thus formed, which may be of wholly different type from the adjacent or underlying primary magma that supplied the heat and gases to form it, may then be forced upward by pressure exerted by the primary magma until it reaches the surface and forms lava. Such palingenetic lava is not identical in composition with the rocks which were melted to form it, because certain constituents,—principally potash, soda, lime and magnesia,—have been contributed to it by the magmatic gases. Palingenetic lavas are usually of somewhat lower temperature than primary lavas, and owe their mobility largely to the gases, which the primary magma has given it, or which were originally contained, in gaseous,

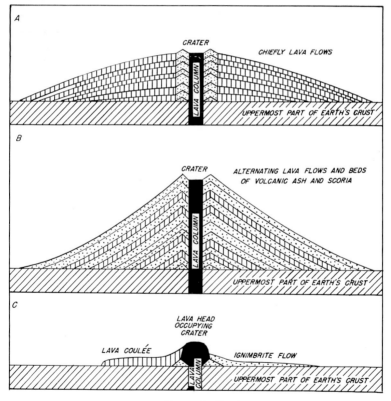

FIGURE 6 - 7

Illustrating diagrammatically the different types of volcanoes.

A. Shield or Hawaiian type.

B. Conical or Vesuvian type.

C. Domical or Peleean type.

liquid or solid form, in the rock formations, which were melted to form it. Such lavas, consequently, are almost always very viscous.

With rare exceptions, all magma reaching the Earth's surface, through the conduits provided by breccia pipes and, to a lesser extent, by dikes, is associated with the surface structures known as volcanoes, which are built up of the products of eruptions. There are three types of volcanoes, depending upon their shape: (1) Shield or Hawaiian type; (2) Conical or Vesuvian type; and (3) Domical or Peleean type.

Shield volcanoes are so called because of their resemblance in shape to an ancient circular shield, with a central boss or protuberance. They are formed by relatively fluid lavas—almost invariably basaltic—and are of relatively low relief. A typical volcano of this class consists of a central steep-sided "cinder cone," composed almost wholly of fragmental ejecta, such as volcanic ash, lapilli and scoria, surrounded by numerous wide-spreading, superimposed lava flows, —the latter considerably exceeding in volume that of the central cinder cone. The lava escapes from the crater of the cinder cone, sometimes by overflowing its rim, but more commonly by breaching the cone on one side or by forcing a way laterally through it. The slope of the surrounding lava flows is usually low, varying from 5° to 10°, and is frequently flatter near the crater than further from it, due to the greater heat and consequent higher fluidity near its point of emission, so that in profile a shield volcano is commonly gently convex. Most volcanoes of this type are small, the central cone being only a few hundred feet in height, but they range from this size up to giant edifices like the volcano of Mauna Loa in the Hawaiian Islands, which rises to a height of about 28,000 ft. above its sub-oceanic base, where it is probably nearly 100 miles in diameter. Most volcanoes of this type do not occur singly but in groups, forming volcanic fields, which comprise numerous individual craters,—up to a hundred or more in some instances. A top example of such a basaltic volcanic field is furnished by the island of Iceland, which has an area of nearly 40,000 square miles, and has been built up, since its commencement in middle Tertiary time, wholly by the contributions of its volcanoes, which number over 100 and of which 24 have been active in historic times. Many similar volcanic fields, formed during the Tertiary period, are known in various parts of the world; and in some instances the individual volcanoes, that created them, were so small and so closely spaced that their lava flows overlapped on their margins, forming nearly horizontal aggregates of flows, covering many thousands of square miles, and accumulating sometimes to depths of several thousand feet. Such aggregates of flows are called "plateau basalts," and are well illustrated by the basaltic lava flows which occupy the extensive Snake River plain of southern Idaho.

While the eroded foundations of old basaltic volcanoes reveal that in most cases they utilized breccia pipes as their conduits, occasionally lava has ascended along dikes occupying fissures, and has caused what are called "fissure eruptions"; but it is not to be understood by this term that the lava merely overflowed the lips of the fissures upon the surface, such as water might do, for invariably one or more cinder cones form along such a fissure, usually at the point or points of lowest or readiest exit, and the lava escapes only from these cones,—the remainder of the fissure being sealed by congealed lava. The largest "fissure eruption" of modern times was that of Skaptar Jökull on the island of Iceland, which took place in the summer of the year 1783. A fissure, called the Laki fissure, opened in a barren plain, where there had been no previous volcanic vent, and provided a conduit for the ascent of basaltic lava in vast quantity. The fissure averaged about 10 ft. in width and extended for a length of twelve miles, along which were built about 100 cinder cones, seldom more than 200 to 300 ft. high, in an almost continuous row. Two great lava streams, one fifty miles in length and the other forty, proceeded from these cinder cones and occupied two river valleys, and the total volume of lava erupted has been estimated at 2.95 cubic miles. The volcanic ash expelled during the eruption, estimated at half a cubic mile in volume, destroyed pasturage over such a large portion of the island, that 52% of all the cattle on the island, 77% of all the horses and 82% of all the sheep died of starvation, in consequence of which 9,500 people,—20% of the entire population,—also succumbed to famine.

Volcanoes of Conical or Vesuvian type,—so-called from the volcano of Vesuvius in Italy,—have the shape usually associated with volcanoes in popular imagination. They are doubly concave in profile, being steepest near the summit, where the slope approaches the angle of repose (about $35°$), and flattening in a sweeping curve towards the base. They are usually composed of lava flows and fragmental ejecta in separate layers. The lava may escape from the summit crater or from rifts on the flanks. The lavas are usually of acidic or intermediate type (rhyolite to andesite) as compared with the dominantly basaltic type of lava constituting the shield

type of volcanoes, and are relatively much less fluid and more viscous. The individual volcanoes of this type are much higher, on
the average, than those of the shield type, not infrequently attaining
elevations of 10,000 ft. above their bases, as exemplified by the
volcano of Mt. Shasta in northern California, and, while they usually
occur in groups, forming volcanic fields, the individual volcanoes
are fewer in number and more widely spaced, on the average, than
those of Shield type. Volcanoes of both Shield and Conical type are
formed by primary lavas exclusively, and there is every degree of
gradation between the two types, depending upon the fluidity and
gas content of the lavas.

Volcanoes of the Domical or Peleean type,—so named from the
volcano of Pelée on the island of Martinique in the West Indies,—
are substantially different from the two types previously described.
The latter always have summit craters when formed, while the
volcanoes of domical type exhibit them only occasionally, because
their lava, which is exceedingly stiff and viscous, usually completely
fills and thus obliterates any craters that may have been formed,
and rises above them in domical masses. Often an eruption consists
solely of the slow welling up of viscous lava into steep-sided, bulbous
domes, called cumulodomes, tholoids or plug-domes; and where the
lava flows away from the craters, it does so sluggishly in the form
of steep-sided flows of great thickness, known as coulees. The lava
of this type of volcanoes is always acidic, and probably nearly always
is of secondary or palingenetic origin, being formed by the melting of
solid rock in place by the heat and gases escaping from underlying
magma of primary origin. Where the gas content of such lava is
low, the lava is usually glassy or stony in appearance, but where
the gas content is high, it tends to cause the lava to be distended by
myriads of gas-filled vesicles, forming a rock of bread-like structure
known as pumice. Pumice, while still in a liquid state, is latently
explosive, due to the fact that the viscosity of the lava tends to
arrest the escape of the gases, which are confined in the vesicles
under pressure; and as the external pressure decreases with approach
to the surface, the internal gas pressure in the vesicles may exceed
the strength of the containing walls, whereupon they are explosively
disrupted into small fragments, which, carried upward by the escaping gases, are dispersed abroad as volcanic ash. Sometimes the
explosive disruption of viscous pumice is progressive, somewhat like
a chain reaction. Thus the disruption of the top portion of a column
of pumiceous lava in a volcanic throat relieves the pressure on the

next underlying section of the pumice column, which thereupon also spontaneously explodes, followed in turn by the next subjacent section, and so on down to a depth where the gas content of the lava is not sufficient to cause it to explode. Thus the column of pumiceous magma in a volcanic throat may progressively but rapidly explode to a considerable depth, completely clearing the crater and the volcanic throat of all lava down to that level. The lava, thus shredded into fragments and expelled violently from the volcanic vent, may be hurled high into the air, and showered down upon the surrounding country, for long distances away from the volcano, as falls of volcanic ash; or, if the explosions are less violent or the exploding pumice more bulky, the explosions may have sufficient force to only lift the fragmental material over the rim of the crater,—somewhat like a pot boiling over,—from which point it flows down the outer slopes of the volcano with great rapidity, somewhat like a lava stream, but instead of being a liquid, it consists of a mixture of red-hot viscous pumice fragments, large and small, and of heated magmatic gases, which these fragments are still evolving. This material, because of the lightness of the pumice, which has a specific gravity less than that of water, and because of the lubrication afforded by the evolving gases, has an extraordinary mobility, sometimes attaining on steep slopes a velocity of a mile a minute, and flowing for distances up to 35 miles. Flows of this nature are known as "nuées ardentes," literally translated "glowing clouds," because of the lofty, dust-laden, cauliflower shaped clouds of liberated hot magmatic gases, which rise from them,—sometimes to heights of 20,000 ft.,—and accompany them on their progress; but a more accurate descriptive term would be "glowing avalanches." On the morning of May 2, 1902, such a glowing avalanche, originating from the crater of the volcano Pelée, on the island of Martinique in the West Indies, sped down the mountainside toward the seaport city of St. Pierre, with some 28,000 inhabitants; and although the avalanche itself did not reach the city, the cloud of scorchingly hot magmatic gases rising from it swept beyond it and over the city, burning to death, within the space of a few minutes, every living person in it with the sole exception of one prisoner in the city jail. A glowing avalanche, when cooled, resembles topographically a very mobile landslide, and consists of a chaotic mixture of pumiceous fragments and dust, known as "ignimbrite." While there is no transitional gradation between volcanoes of Peleean type and those of Hawaiian and Vesuvian types, domical volcanoes of the former type are sometimes found to be parasitic upon the flanks of volcanoes of the Vesuvian type, and occasionally such a domical volcano usurps the throat and crater of an extinct or dormant volcano of the Vesuvian type and thus succeeds it.

There is a special type of volcanic structure, known as a "caldera," which is distinguished from a normal volcano by its different mode of origin, its usually much larger crater, and its somewhat different topographic form. The term is borrowed from the volcano of La Caldera, on the island of Palma, Canary Islands, whose crater is three to four miles across, and whose rim rises 5,000 ft. above its floor. Caldera is a Spanish word, meaning cauldron or large kettle, and was applied in this instance because of the size and shape of the crater. There are three types of calderas: (1) Explosion calderas; (2) Collapse calderas; and (3) Subsidence calderas.

An explosion caldera represents the crater-like surface structure created by the formation of an explosion pipe, as described on page 169. It is formed when the subterranean pressure of magmatic gases, distributed through the upper part of an underlying mass of magma, exceeds the strength of the crust at that point, whereupon a hole is blown through, creating a pipe-like opening, which is occupied by the chaotic breccia formed by the explosion, while a crater-like ring of the same material encircles the mouth of the pipe at the surface. Such an explosion caldera is distinguished from a normal volcanic crater by the fact that the latter is perched at the top of a volcanic cone, usually at some height above the surrounding country, is funnel-shaped, and commonly is relatively small compared with the bulk of the mountain; whereas the floor of an explosion caldera is usually somewhat below the level of the surrounding country, the size of the interior of the caldera is large compared with the volume of the ring of debris surrounding it, and the caldera is somewhat bowl-shaped, having a relatively large width compared to its depth. Also, while a normal volcanic cone is composed wholly of igneous material, an explosion caldera ring may contain no igneous material whatever, but only fragments of the rock formations penetrated by the pipe, which may be exclusively sedimentary. An explosion caldera often provides a convenient conduit for the later ascent of lava, through the explosion breccia occupying the pipe thus created, forming a volcano of Hawaiian or Vesuvian type within the caldera and thus creating what may be called cone-in-bowl structure. The impact of a large meteorite may create a crater, closely resembling superficially an explosion caldera, such as the "Meteor Crater" in

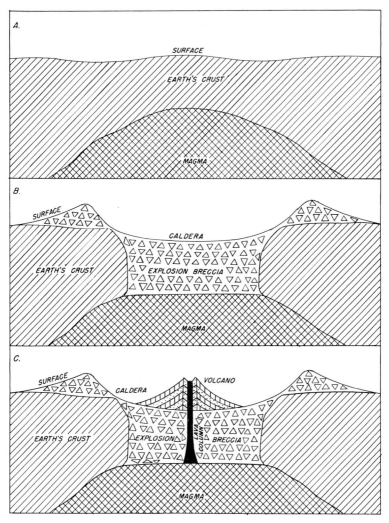

FIGURE 6 - 8

Illustrating diagrammatically the mode of formation of an explosion caldera and of cone-in-bowl structure.

Coconino County, Arizona; but such structures are very rare, and can usually be identified by the presence of meteorite fragments among the debris forming the crater ring. Probably the largest explosion caldera in the United States is "Kilbourne's Hole," in Dona Ana County, New Mexico, the bottom of which is nearly flat and is about two miles long by a mile and a half wide. An example of cone-in-bowl structure is provided by the "Zuni Crater," in Catron County, New Mexico, which is about a mile in diameter, and contains a small interior basaltic cinder cone.

There are two types of collapse calderas: (1) one formed by the lateral drainage of the lava column in a volcanic throat to a lower level, thus emptying the upper part of the volcanic throat, into which the upper part of the volcanic cone collapses, forming a caldera; and (2) one formed by the explosive demolition of a column of pumiceous lava, creating a void into which the upper part of the volcanic cone collapses, forming a caldera.

A collapse caldera of the first type is formed in the following way. In a volcano of normal type, the walls of the cone are often riven by radial fractures, created either by explosions or by pressure of the central lava column; and in such case the lava occupying the throat of the volcano sometimes finds its way, along such a radial fracture, to the surface on the side of the cone, and, there issuing, flows down its flanks. In this process, the column of lava occupying the volcanic throat is lowered to the level of lateral escape, and this withdraws the support previously afforded by it to the walls of the throat down to this point, so that they sometimes cave into the void thus created, involving in the collapse the upper part of the volcanic cone, and creating a caldera much larger than the original summit crater and lying at a lower elevation. An example of a collapse caldera formed in this manner is provided by the Mokuaweoweo crater of the volcano of Mauna Loa in the Hawaiian Islands. This crater is nearly three miles in length by two miles in width at its widest part, and is enclosed by vertical cliffs ranging from 500 to 600 ft. in height. Subsequent resumption of the ascent of lava up the volcanic throat may form a small volcano of Hawaiian or Vesuvian type within the caldera and thus create a cone-in-bowl structure.

Collapse calderas of the second type are, like the first, always confined to pre-existing volcanoes, usually of Vesuvian type, and are formed when, up or alongside the throat of the volcano, there ascends a very silicious, very viscous, highly gas-charged magma, which expands into pumiceous lava near the surface. This lava is usually different in composition from the type of lava, which the volcano had previously discharged, and is probably always of palingenetic origin. When such a lava column has approached sufficiently close to the surface, so that the external pressure on the column is less than the internal gas pressure, it disintegrates explosively to a con-

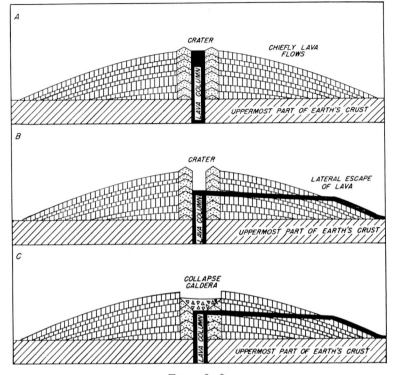

FIGURE 6 - 9

Illustrating diagrammatically the mode of formation of a collapse caldera, due to drainage of the lava column in a volcanic throat to a lower level.

siderable depth, usually in successive paroxysms spaced from a few minutes to a few hours apart, as previously described on page 177. The expansive effect of the explosion is sufficiently damped by the weight of the material disintegrated so that the result is a sort of heave, which lifts the disintegrated lava over the rim of the crater, down whose outer slopes it then flows swiftly as glowing avalanches. In this manner the throat occupied by the lava column is completely cleared of the lava to a very considerable depth in a very short period of time, whereupon the walls of the throat, weakened by the explosions and lacking the supporting pressure of the lava column, cave into the void thus created, engulfing in their collapse the entire upper part of the mountain. The former volcanic cone of Vesuvian type is thus eviscerated, leaving only its base, which is occupied by a caldera, much larger than the original summit crater and lying at a much lower level. Such a collapse caldera is always flanked on the lower slopes of the volcano, whose former body it occupies, by flows of ignimbrite, which represent the original glowing avalanches. It will be recognized that the mechanics of this process

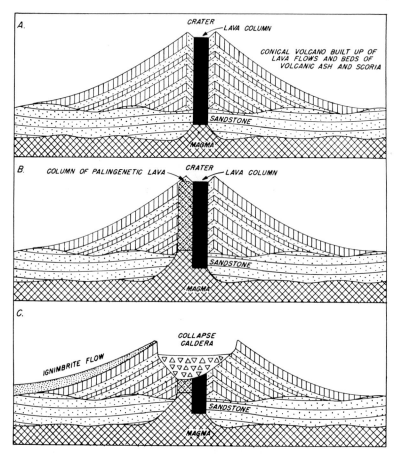

FIGURE 6 - 10

Illustrating diagrammatically the mode of formation of a collapse caldera, due to explosive demolition of a column of pumiceous palingenetic lava.

are similar to those of the formation of a collapse caldera of the first type, except that in the present instance the void is created by the explosive demolition of a lava column, instead of by lateral drainage of a lava column to a lower level. A cone-in-bowl structure may be created in a caldera of this sort by subsequent resumption of the ascent of the original lava.

Since palingenetic lava is explosive only when highly gas-charged and very viscous, and since the latter condition occurs only when it is very silicious in composition, there is reason to suspect that, in many cases where collapse calderas of this type have been formed, the rocks melted in place to form such a magma consisted chiefly of sandstones, conglomerates or arkoses; since such highly silicious sedimentary rocks are exceptionally porous, and may contain considerable percentages of water,—either connate water, which was entrapped between the sand grains and pebbles at the time of deposition beneath the surface of the sea or other body of water, or artesian water entering from the surface and percolating along the beds. Thus, such sedimentary rocks may contain up to 10% water, as compared with most massive igneous rocks which usually contain no more than from 1% to 5%; while also, because of their porosity, they can more readily receive contributions of gases from underlying magmas. The silicious character of such sediments renders the resulting palingenetic magma, derived from their melting, very viscous, and this circumstance, together with the high gas content, resulting from the conversion of the original water content into steam, plus the magmatic gases contributed by underlying magma, cause it to be highly explosive, when transformed into pumice. The addition of some potash, soda, lime and magnesia, present in the magmatic gases—probably in the form of chlorides,—to the palingenetic lava, changes its composition somewhat from what it would be if it resulted only from the melting of sedimentary rocks, and renders it more fusible. The caldera of Katmai in southern Alaska, which occupies the former volcano of that name and was formed in 1912 by an eruption of utmost violence, is underlaid by silicious sedimentary formations of Jurassic age, and probably owes its origin to this circumstance, according to the mode of formation described above; and there is reason to believe that the same significant association has been responsible for the formation of other similar calderas.

Some of the most destructive eruptions of historic times have occurred in the course of the formation of collapse calderas of this type. Thus an eruption in the small volcanic island of Krakatau, in Sunda strait between the islands of Java and Sumatra, in the East Indies, culminated in the latter part of August in 1883 in paroxysmal explosions, which demolished the whole northern half of the island, and created in its place a large submarine depression, which was 1,000 ft. deep in places. Giant waves, formed by the explosions, swept away a hundred villages on the shores of neighboring islands, and drowned some 36,000 people. The sea for miles around was covered with floating bodies and fragments of pumice. Some 4.3 cubic miles of material were expelled, of which about 5% consisted of fragments of old lava composing the original volcanic cone, while the remainder was new and more silicious lava evacuated from below. This mass of new magna must have risen, not through the old volcanic throat but alongside it, as the caldera is excentric with respect to the original volcano. Forty four years later a new basaltic cone, rising from the floor of the caldera, made its appearance above the surface of the sea, forming a cone-in-bowl structure. The best example of a collapse caldera in the United States, and the most recent, although formed in prehistoric times, is the spectacular abyss of Crater Lake in southern Oregon. At its rim it is four miles wide and five miles long, with a depth of about 3,000 ft., the lower third of which is filled with water. The ignimbrite flows formed contemporaneously are particularly large and impressive, one of them being 35 miles in length. Within the caldera is a small later andesitic volcanic cone of Vesuvian type, forming a cone-in-bowl structure.

While collapse calderas, as previously described, are confined to individual volcanoes, subsidence calderas formed by the vertical escape of magma to the surface, either within the area of the caldera or to one side of it, are not limited to individual volcanoes but may occupy a much larger area. Such a subsidence caldera is formed over a body of magma of considerable areal extent, such as a thick sill, a laccolith or a broad-topped cupola. Penetration of the roof of such a satellitic structure allows the escape of magma upward to reach the surface and there form a volcano; and the levitative effect of the gases entrapped in the magma lessens its specific gravity, and thereby allows it to rise higher than would be possible, if due simply to the weight of the superincumbent formations. The magma in a large subterranean pool, formed by a thick sill, a laccolith or a batholithic cupola, may, therefore, move laterally for some distance to ascend a volcanic vent, and in this way may withdraw support from a more or less circular area of considerable size. The magma thus withdrawn, after ascending to the surface, tends to accumulate there in the form of lava flows and other volcanic products, thereby adding weight to the sinking area and accentuating the process. In this manner a more or less circular sinking area, bounded by a ring fault, is formed. The creation of a subsidence caldera in this way is a slow process, and not catastrophic like the formation of other types of calderas, since it is gradually accomplished, extending over a considerable period of time, and, when erosion keeps pace with the sinking, it may lack topographic expression. A caldera of this nature is different from the other types of calderas, previously described, in that no large surface crater is formed, and, in fact, its existence is often discovered only by geological mapping, which reveals the discordance between the positions of the formations within and without it.

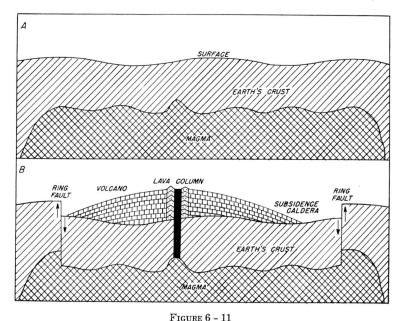

FIGURE 6 - 11

Illustrating diagrammatically the mode of formation of a subsidence caldera, or ring graben,—disregarding erosion.

An example of such a subsidence caldera, formed by the transference of underlying magma to the surface through volcanic vents, is the Silverton caldera, in southwestern Colorado, where a roughly circular area, about eight miles in diameter, has sunk to a depth of from 2,000 to 2,500 feet below the original surface. Smaller subsidence calderas may also be formed by the removal of overlying rock in the form of gaseous products, similar to the formation of collapse breccia pipes, as described on page 169. The Ball Mt. caldera, in the Leadville Mining District, Lake County, Colorado, which constitutes an elliptical area about a mile and a half in length by three quarters of a mile in width, that has sunk a distance of about 1,200 ft., has apparently been formed in this manner, as there is no evidence of any transfer of subterranean magma to the surface in or adjacent to this locality. "Ring graben" is an alternative name sometimes used for a subsidence caldera.

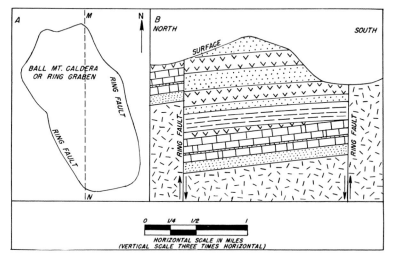

FIGURE 6 - 12

(A) Surface plan and (B) diagrammatic cross-section, along line MN, of the Ball Mt. caldera or ring graben, Leadville Mining District, Lake County, Colorado.

A transfer of magma from lower levels in the Earth's Crust,— not to its surface, however, but to higher horizons in the Crust,— accompanied by the subsidence of a more or less circular area, occurs in the formation of lopoliths, which are thick sills, concave towards their centers where their feeding conduits are situated, forming basin-like structures, which involve not only the sills them- selves but also the overlying and underlying formations. In this case, the withdrawal of material from an underlying batholith, and its transfer to a sill higher in the Earth's Crust, causes a sagging of the formations intruded by the sill, but these formations still remain attached on their edges, and there is no actual rupture, forming a ring fault, surrounding the sinking area, as in the case of a sub- sidence caldera or ring graben. The mechanics of the process are similar to the formation of a laccolith, except that the shape of the intrusive mass is different,—a laccolith being plano-convex in cross- section, with the convex side uppermost, while a lopolith is con- cave, both at top and at bottom, in cross-section. Lopoliths are always formed by basic or ultrabasic magmas, and may attain large dimensions, up to a thickness of several thousand feet and a diameter of more than forty miles. They are usually accompanied by more or less palingenetic melting and assimilation of the roof formations, as described on page 162. The Sudbury basin in the Province of Ontario, Canada, provides a good example of a lopolith.

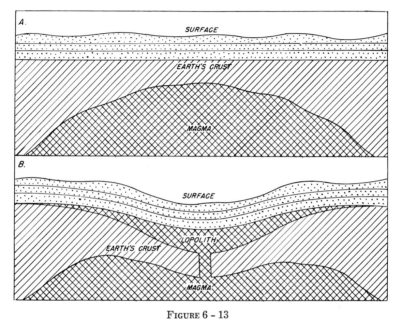

FIGURE 6 - 13

Illustrating diagrammatically the mode of formation of a lopolith.

While the primary cause of vulcanism is pressure from below, due to expansion of the Earth's interior caused by disintegration of high density atoms constituting its central Nucleus, magmatic gases play an important role in the surface phenomena of vulcanism, as illustrated by the eruption of Vesuvius in 1906. This Italian volcano, like most other so-called active volcanoes, is dormant more than 99% of the time, and its periods of eruption are tempestuous but brief. The eruption of 1906, which terminated a thirty-four year period of dormancy since the last previous major eruption in 1872, lasted only eighteen days, divided into three phases: the first or luminous liquid lava phase, which lasted four days; the second or intermediate gas phase, which lasted twelve hours; and the third or dark ash phase, which consumed the remainder of the time. At the commencement of the eruption, the throat of the volcano was filled to the top with a column of lava, of which the uppermost 2,000 ft. or so consisted of

white-hot, very liquid lava at a probable temperature of about 1,200°
C. Below this was viscous, pasty primary magma, probably several
hundred degrees cooler than the overlying liquid lava, and extending
down to the underlying magma chamber. During the long period of
dormancy, bubbles of magmatic gases had been collecting in the lava
column occupying the volcanic throat, and some of these gases in
their upward movement entered into exothermic or heat-producing
combinations with each other, thereby heating the lava in the upper
part of the column and converting it into more fluid form. This
more fluid lava, occupying the upper part of the column, acted like
a cork, restraining by its presence the escape of gases from the subjacent pasty lava, in the top part of which, therefore, further acces-
sions of gases tended to accumulate. This equilibrium was terminated by the formation of a fissure in the side of the volcanic cone,
which tapped the lava column 1,300 ft. below its top and allowed
the more fluid lava above this level to escape to the surface, thereby
reducing the pressure upon the gases imprisoned in the top part of
the underlying viscous lava; and these gases at once started to escape
in large volume, violently churning the more fluid lava still remaining
in the volcanic throat, and causing the formation of brilliant foun-
tains of incandescent lava. At the culmination of this phase of the
eruption, a fiery column of lava, emulsified by gases, a thousand feet
in diameter, rose to a height of two miles above the crater, and in
its fall clothed the entire top of the mountain with a glowing mantle.
Upon the complete expulsion of all the more fluid lava from the
throat of the volcano in this manner, this phase of the eruption
terminated, but the magmatic gases imprisoned in the viscous magma
continued to escape in still higher volume and with still greater
velocity, to the accompaniment of violent explosions. The situation
was like the uncorking of a bottle of soda water, whereupon the
gases, previously contained under pressure in the liquid, expand and
separate, effervescing through the neck of the bottle. These escaping
gases, emerging from the volcanic throat with a roar like the blowing
off of a gigantic boiler, formed a whitish column shaped like an
inverted cone, six miles in height and ranging in diameter from
1,300 ft. at the bottom to two miles at the top, above which level the
gases spread laterally in the form of white, cauliflower shaped
clouds. The outrushing gas contained considerable ash, which, however, was so dwarfed by the volume of the gas that it was hardly
noticeable. At the end of twelve hours of this second phase, the
volume of escaping gases fell off abruptly, and during the remainder

of the eruption the ascending gases, highly charged with dark ash, billowed slowly aloft in a dark column, which expanded rapidly in size as it mounted. While, therefore, the principal source of igneous activity is pressure from below, the chief cause of a volcanic eruption, which is only a minor form of igneous activity, is the escape of magmatic gases, previously accumulated below a volcanic cone during a long period of slow ascent through the underlying magma or of slow release by assimilated wall rock. The eruptions of Vesuvius are unusually spectacular, because its emission of magmatic gases is exceptionally voluminous. This is due to the fact that the volcano rests upon a platform of sedimentary formations, consisting largely of beds of limestone and dolomite; and these rocks, upon assimilation by the underlying magmatic reservoir, contribute carbon dioxide in large volume to it. The gases expelled by Vesuvius during eruptions consist mainly of water vapor and carbon dioxide.

As has been previously stated, volcanoes are usually grouped in areas termed volcanic fields, which contain from a few to many volcanoes. Such volcanic fields are of two types: (1) those in which the grouping, both as regards distribution and age relationship, is irregular, although tending to form more or less circular or elliptical tracts; and (2) those in which, in both respects, the grouping is distinctly linear. In the first the volcanoes probably overlie and are fed from a broad pool of magma, usually a thick sill or a laccolith, which is relatively stationary,—new orifices in the roof of this pool being created for the formation of new volcanoes, when, owing to the plugging of the conduits or the depletion of the gas content of the magma immediately below, older volcanoes become extinct. In the second or linear type of volcanic field, the underlying pressure column migrates slowly in one direction, while the formation of new volcanoes keeps pace with its progress. In such case, the oldest and longest extinct volcanoes lie furthest to the rear, and the volcanoes become progressively younger in the direction of advance,—active volcanoes being clustered about its head. An excellent illustration of this is furnished by the Hawaiian Islands, where the underlying body of magma seems to have moved slowly southeasterly for a distance of about 1,600 miles. At the northwestern end of the long submarine ridge, of which islands represent the higher summits, the greatest erosion has taken place, indicating the greatest age. In a southeasterly direction, therefore, the extinct volcanoes become progressively more recent, until the only active volcanoes,—Mauna Loa and Kilauea,—are situated on the island of Hawaii, furthest to the southeast, which is the youngest island and also the largest, having suffered marine erosion for the least time. The advance of such a chain of volcanoes is very slow and takes considerable time, from a geological standpoint. Thus, in the case of the Hawaiian Islands, igneous activity probably commenced not later than middle Tertiary and has continued uninterruptedly down to the present time.

Orogeny, the process of non-volcanic mountain building, is a by-product of vulcanism, although it is not always associated with surface volcanic activity. Orogeny manifests itself in many diverse ways and on a wide range of scale. Volcanoes and calderas, which are directly caused by igneous extrusives, are excluded from consideration under the term orogeny, but it comprises such mountain forms as domes, fault elevated tracts and folded or arcuate mountain ranges, all of which are caused by the upward pressure of hidden, deep-seated intrusive masses.

The most common forms of orogenic structures are domes, of which there are three types, as shown on the accompanying illustration. An invariable feature of the formation of domes is an expansion in surface area, and the division of domes into three kinds depends on the ways in which this expansion of surface area is brought about. The simplest type of domes is that in which the expansion of surface area is accompanied by stretching of the formations involved in the dome. Such domes may be caused by laccolithic igneous intrusions or by upward bulging of deeper batholithic masses. The domical structures, which serve as oil traps, belong to this class. In domes of the second division, the stretching of the formations is aided by peripheral normal faulting, which causes such domes to have somewhat abrupt margins. Domes of this type are as a whole larger than those of the preceding class, and are probably in most cases caused by upward batholithic bulging. In domes of the third type the surface expansion is brought about largely by the subsidence, at the summit of the dome, of a linear fault block, wedge-shaped in cross-section, bounded between two normal faults dipping toward each other, and creating what is known as a graben or rift valley. Domes of this class are the largest of all, and may be several hundred miles in diameter, while the central graben may drop as much as two miles. They are doubtless invariably due to batholithic bulging. Examples are supplied by the Red Sea rift valley, between Arabia and Ethiopia; the Dead Sea graben of Palestine; the Rhine graben of Germany; the rift valleys of central Africa; and the num-

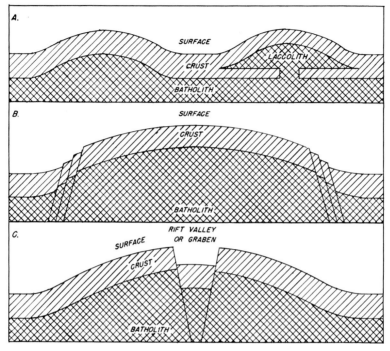

FIGURE 6 - 14

Types of domes: (A) Of batholithic or laccolithic origin, accomplished by stretching of the formations of the Crust; (B) Of batholithic origin, accomplished by stretching of the formations of the Crust, accompanied by peripheral normal faulting; (C) Of batholithic origin, accomplished by stretching of the formations of the Crust, accompanied by the formation of a graben or rift valley at the summit of the dome.

erous parallel grabens of the Great Basin of the United States, lying between the Sierra Nevada Range and the Rocky Mountains, and extending north into Canada. One frequent feature of the larger and deeper rift valleys is the presence of basaltic volcanoes in them, indicating that the crustal disturbance has extended sufficiently deep to tap basaltic intrusive bodies.

Another manifestation of upward pressure, exerted by pressure columns in the Earth's Crust, is the vertical lifting of certain tracts surrounded by ring faults. Such elevated tracts vary widely in size. An example of a relatively small one is afforded by an elliptical tract, ranging from nine to fifteen miles in diameter, situated in the Front Range of Colorado, with Pike's Peak its culminating point. It has been elevated bodily several thousand feet above the sur-

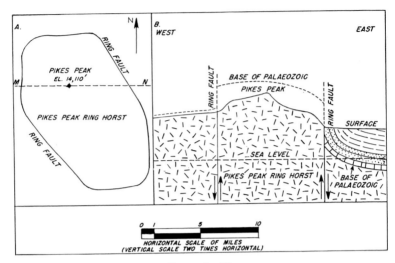

FIGURE 6 - 15

(A) Surface plan and (B) diagrammatic cross-section, along line MN, of the
Pike's Peak ring horst or elevated fault block, El Paso and Teller counties,
Colorado.

rounding country, forming a ring horst, as shown in the accompanying illustration. At the other limit, as to size, may be the continent
of Antarctica, or a large portion of it, which rises from ocean depths
of from one to two miles, surrounding it on all sides. In the case of
an elevated tract of such large area, it may have been formed by
several pressure columns, which were of large size, and may have
migrated about, progressively elevating it in sections.

The most impressive manifestations of orogeny, as well as some
of the largest, occur in the formation of the so-called folded or
arcuate mountain ranges, some of which extend for distances of
more than a thousand miles. These folded mountain ranges are
formed by the conversion of upward vertical pressure by a pressure
column into lateral pressure in one direction, thereby causing folding
and thrust faulting of the uppermost portions of the Earth's Crust,
as discussed on pages 143 and 146 and illustrated in Figures 5 - 7
and 5 - 9. One common feature of these folded mountain ranges is
the formation, directly ahead of their direction of growth, of a trough
or depression in the Earth's Crust, called a foredeep, which is probably caused by the piling up of pressure behind. Examples of such
folded mountain ranges are the Alps, where the pressure came from
the north, and the buried foredeep is occupied by the valley of the

Po River; the Andes Mountains, where the pressure came from the east, and the foredeep lies directly offshore in the Pacific Ocean; and the Himalayas, where the pressure came from the north, and the buried foredeep in covered by the plains of India at its southern base. A folded mountain range is not formed all at one time by a pressure column of comparable size, but progressively by a smaller pressure column, which, starting at one end, gradually migrates toward the other. The mechanics are somewhat like those exerted in the formation of a linear volcanic field, as described on page 189. The Alps have stopped growing and constitute a finished mountain range, and the Andes have nearly reached the same end; but the elevation of the Himalayas is still progressing in its westerly extension, the Hindu Kush mountains. One indication of the current growth of a folded mountain range is the occurrence of deep earthquakes in the upper part of its pressure column, where it penetrates the top portion of the Earth's Mantle. Thus, in the past forty years, at least 70 deep earthquakes have originated from nearly the same source, at a depth of about 230 kilometers, beneath the Hindu Kush range. No folded mountain range is in process of formation in the United States and Canada at the present time, and consequently no deep earthquakes are occurring in this area. The Appalachian Mountains form the eroded roots of such a mountain range, which was formed during the Carboniferous era,—the pressure coming from the east, from a large granitic batholith now exposed by erosion, so that the folds and thrust faults were formed on its western side. The growth of several folded mountain ranges is in progress at the present time along the western side of the Pacific Ocean, ranging from Kamchatka through Japan down to the East Indies.

Pressure columns in the Earth's body are in some respects the counterparts of the solar cyclones, which form sunspots on the Sun's surface, for both are directly caused by the disintegration of centrally situated high density atoms (Q-atoms); but they differ through the fact that in the Sun some of the end products of this disintegration actually rise through the body of the Sun to its surface by means of these solar cyclones, while in the Earth there is no similar upward movement of material in the pressure columns, but only a transmission of pressure upward. Sunspots on the Sun are almost wholly confined to a central zone extending to 45° latitude north and south of its equator,—a circumstance which may be due to the effect of the centrifugal force generated in this zone by the Sun's rotation. A somewhat similar but less conspicuous association may be observed on the surface of the Earth, where the volcanic fields are concentrated chiefly in the equatorial zone and adjacent halves of the north and south temperate zones,—decreasing in abundance polewards in each direction. No active volcano is at present known to occur within the Arctic Circle, and only one—the volcano Erebus on the shores of the Antarctic continent,—within the Antarctic circle.

Oddly enough, some of the most important evidence relative to the internal structure of the Earth is supplied by its consort, the Moon, which, while commonly designated a satellite, is more probably a twin planet, separated from the Earth by fission of a common planetary mass born of the Sun. In the course of its monthly revolution around the Earth,—or, more properly, around the common center of gravity of the Earth and Moon,—the Moon makes one complete rotation on its own axis, and so always keeps the same side turned toward the Earth. Due to small oscillations in the Moon's movements, with reference to the Earth, however, additional parts of its surface are occasionally visible, making a total of about 60% of the Moon's surface which may be seen from the Earth at one time or another, and leaving about 40% which is permanently hidden. Because of the relative proximity of the Moon in space, the features of that part of its surface, which is turned toward the Earth, are readily visible to telescopic observation, down to structures less than half a mile in diameter; and a comparison of the surface features of the Earth and the Moon reveal some significant similarities and differences. Because of the much smaller size and mass of the Moon, its surface attraction is not enough to prevent the escape of atmospheric gases and water vapor into space. Consequently the Moon has no atmosphere and no surface bodies of water. Therefore no erosion can take place on its surface; no sedimentary formations of aqueous origin can be formed, in the absence of bodies of water; and no aeolian deposits can be created, in the absence of winds. The surface of the Moon, therefore, is composed wholly of rocks of igneous origin,—either lava flows or fragmental material originating from volcanic explosions. The only force acting to break down the rocks of the lunar surface is the heat of the Sun, which, during the lunar day, raises the temperature to about 100° C.,—the boiling point of water at sea-level on the Earth,—while during the lunar night the temperature must fall nearly to that of surrounding space, or about —273° C. This tremendous variation in temperature doubtless results in alternate expansion and contraction of the surface rocks, causing them to crack and disintegrate; but the only move-ment would be a slow downward creep on the slopes, not of sufficient extent to work any great changes in topography. As a result, while topographic forms are not long lived, geologically speaking, on the Earth, they tend to remain unchanged on the Moon for vast periods of time, unless destroyed, modified or buried by subsequent volcanic activity. It is possible that some of the structures on the surface of the Moon, now visible, date back to the equivalent of the Archeozoic era on the Earth.

The surface of the Moon shows two kinds of colors, about equal in extent,—lighter-hued areas, which are rough and mountainous, and represent the uplands of the Moon; and darker-hued areas (constituting the eyes, nose and gaping mouth of the "Man-in-the-Moon"), which are plains, and represent the lowlands of the Moon. The early astronomers, surveying the Moon through small telescopes, supposed the former to be land areas and the latter to be bodies of water; but it is now known the the darker-hued areas are also land, and that the color contrast between the two is due to differences in their mode of formation and in chemical composition.

In the process of the solidification of the Moon from an early liquid condition, paralleling the early history of the Earth, it is reasonable to assume that there was, to some extent, a gravitative separation of lighter substances from heavier ones, so that the crust of the Moon, like that of the Earth, is composed of lighter and more silicious rocks, as compared with the heavier and more basic rocks in its interior. The rocks composing the lighter-hued areas of the Moon are probably of acidic or intermediate composition, as the color and ruggedness of the terrain suggests, and may represent the original crust, more or less modified by subsequent volcanic activity; while the darker areas, which are of later age, as shown by their encroachment upon the lighter areas and partial burial of structures therein, represent vast fields of lava—doubtless basaltic—compar-able to the plateau basaltic lava fields of the Earth. The magmatic sequence in the lunar extrusives, therefore, has been the same as on the Earth,—the earliest activity being of acidic and intermediate type, followed later by basaltic eruptions as the deeper seated basaltic magma eventually reached the surface, but the lunar se-quence has been Moon-wide, instead of recurring in individual volcanic fields, as on the Earth.

The most conspicuous volcanic structures on the Moon are the so-called giant lunar craters, which are actually calderas, exhibiting the same features as similar structures on the Earth, being large circular or elliptical bowl-shaped structures, in which the size of the craters is large, as compared with the volumes of the rims, and the bottoms of the craters are below the level of the surrounding country, unless partially filled up by later volcanic activity. In many of these calderas there are one or more centrally located conical volcanoes of normal type, constituting the cone-in-bowl structure, which is so conspicuous a feature of many terrestrial calderas. Many of the lunar calderas are of vast size, some of them exceeding a hundred miles in diameter, but they are not disproportionate in this respect to terrestrial calderas, when consideration is given to the much smaller surface gravity of the Moon, and the absence of an atmosphere to retard the aerial flight of explosively propelled fragments, so that a volcanic explosion on the Moon may have more than six times the dimensional results of one of equal force on the Earth. Thus, for sake of comparison, the largest known terrestrial calderas are Mount Asosan on the island of Kiushiu in Japan; Lake Bombom on the island of Luzon in the Philippines; and a nameless crater in northern Kamchatka; each of which is about fifteen miles in diameter. Most of the lunar calderas, especially the larger ones, are located in the lighter-hued areas, and are of earlier age than the basaltic lava flows forming the darker-hued areas, which invade them; but some of the smaller calderas are younger than the basaltic eruptions.

On the Earth, collapse and subsidence calderas are formed only on earlier volcanoes of normal type, similar to some which exist unchanged in the vicinity to illustrate what the calderas originated from; but on the Moon no normal volcanoes exist, comparable in size of ground plan with the calderas, from which it is concluded that the lunar calderas,—or at least all of the larger ones,—are not of collapse or subsidence origin, but have been formed by explosion. Further evidence in support of this conclusion is afforded by the fact that, where there has been no subsequent crater filling, the volume of a caldera crater below the level of the surrounding country is about equal to the volume of the rim above the surrounding country, with due allowance for the expansion of volume resulting from the change from solid rock to broken rock. Such a relationship is characteristic of explosion calderas.

Normal volcanoes of Shield or Hawaiian type, consisting of relatively small central cinder cones, surrounded by extensive basaltic lava flows, abound on the Moon, but most of them are so small and inconspicuous, that they can be recognized only by careful scrutiny under favorable conditions of visibility. The lava plains, in which they occur, are, as on the Earth, built up of a great number of limited eruptions from numerous small local vents,—the lava flows overlapping one another on their margins and thus creating the illusion of a large homogenous formation. The abundance of these small volcanic vents is illustrated by the case of the caldera Plato, which is about sixty miles in diameter, with its rim rising from 5,000 to 7,000 ft. above the surrounding country. It has a smooth, dark-hued floor, lying about 3,000 ft. above the surrounding country, and consisting of basaltic lava flows, which have filled the crater,—originally much deeper,—up to this level. On this floor over forty small craters, ranging from a few hundred feet to a mile in diameter, have been observed; and these craterlets have obviously been the sources of the last basaltic lava flows.

Normal volcanoes of the Conical or Vesuvian type, which have small, high-perched craters at their summits, and which have doubtless been built up, like terrestrial volcanoes of the same type, of alternate flows of lava and beds of volcanic ash and agglomerate of acidic or intermediate type, are not uncommon on the Moon, but they are so much dwarfed by the giant calderas, that they are not conspicuous objects. The most obvious of these volcanoes are the peaks, single or multiple, which occupy the centers of so many of the calderas, constituting cone-in-bowl structure. Many of these show small summit craters, and those which do not may have had their craters filled by ejecta from later volcanoes, or by the creep of the surface rocks. One of the most notable of the volcanoes of this type, outside of the calderas, is the isolated mountain known as Pico, which is about 8,000 ft. in height, and has three peaks, in at least one of which a summit crater is visible.

Volcanoes of Domical or Peleean type cannot be positively identified on the Moon, but their existence is made probable by the phenomena of the so-called ray systems,—some thirty-eight in number,—which radiate from scattered points on the Moon's surface. The individual rays are very light colored, and usually do not exceed five miles in width or from ten to sixty miles in length, although some of them are hundreds of miles long. The largest of these ray systems is that which seems to radiate from the caldera Tycho in the southern hemisphere of the Moon. Some of its rays are over a thousand miles in length, and, at the time of the full Moon, this system gives the Moon a "peeled orange" aspect, which sometimes can be seen by the naked eye. The focal point of each ray system, wherever it can be determined, is one or more minute, intensely white craterlets, seldom over a mile in diameter and usually much less, surrounded by an irregular white blotch, from which the rays emerge. The individual rays are very brilliant near their sources in the white blotches and grow fainter as they recede from it. They are purely superficial phenomena, extending unchanged in straight lines over all kinds of terrain, rough or smooth, light-hued and dark-hued alike, and appear to be of relatively late origin. The explanation, which seems to best fit all the facts, is that the white blotches and the rays that radiate from them represent thin coverings of whitish, silicious volcanic ash, projected away in all directions from exploding pumiceous volcanoes of Peleean type, since similar irregular sheets of white volcanic ash surround similar terrestrial volcanoes.

Plate XIX, which covers a part of the northeastern quadrant of the Moon, shows the extensive dark-hued, doubtless basaltic lava field, known as the Imbrian plain, which covers about 350,000 square miles, as compared with a basaltic plain in the northwestern part of the United States, covering about 150,000 square miles, and another in India of about the same size. At the bottom of the photograph is the giant caldera Copernicus, which is 56 miles in diameter, and whose walls rise 12,000 ft. above the crater floor, which is 8,000 ft. below the level of the surrounding country. The central mountain, which forms the cone-in-bowl structure, consists of five principal peaks, which attain a height of about 2,400 ft. above the crater floor. Terraces, representing landslide blocks, are visible on the inside of the crater walls, while an irregular line of small craterlets, probably formed along a dike, straggles down the northwest outer slope. Copernicus is covered with a thin mantle of white volcanic ash, which appears as a central blotch, dividing into rays with distance away from it. The source of this fall of volcanic ash is a number of small craterlets in and around the caldera. Beyond the northern edge of the Imbrian plain is the large, smooth-floored caldera of Plato, while below it, springing from the Imbrian plain, is the conical volcano Pico,—both of which structures have been previously referred to.

It has been suggested by some scientists that the crater-like structures visible on the face of the Moon may have been formed by the impact of meteorites and not by volcanic activity. Some of the landscape features, however, such as the cone-in-bowl struc-

PLATE XVIII

Photograph of the northwest and southwest quadrants of the Moon, showing the rough, caldera-pitted uplands (light-hued areas), and the relatively smooth surface of the basaltic lava plains (dark-hued areas).

PLATE XIX

Photograph of part of the northeastern quadrant of the Moon, showing the large basaltic lava plain constituting the *"Imbrian Plain,"* and neighboring calderas.

ture and the isolated conical volcanoes, could not have been formed by external impact. The principal objection to this theory is that, if the Moon was ever bombarded by meteorites so plentiful and of such giant size, as would be necessary to account for its pitted surface, the Earth, because of its proximity, should also have shared in the bombardment, but there is no geological evidence to show that such an occurrence ever took place. Craters of proven meteoric origin on the Earth's surface are scarce and small,—the largest known being only 4/5ths of a mile in diameter, while most are far smaller; and if such a meteoric shower ever took place in some past geological period, some evidence of it should be recognizable in the form of meteoric masses imbedded in the formations of that period, but there is no such known occurrence. On the other hand, if vulcanism exists on the Earth and is manifested by certain landscape forms on its surface, it should also exist and be somewhat similarly indicated on the Moon, which, as

PLATE XX

Photograph of part of the southwestern quadrant of the Moon, showing detail of part of the caldera-pitted upland, and the cone-in-bowl structure in the caldera Theophilus, at upper right.

a sister planet, is presumptively similarly constituted; and such appears to be the case. There is no evidence whatever, therefore, to support the meteoric theory of the origin of the Moon's craters, but much to indicate that they have been caused by lunar vulcanism.

The purpose of discussing the lunar volcanic system in so much detail is to make plain that the volcanic history of the Moon closely parallels that of the Earth, with due regard to the initial difference in the sizes of these two related heavenly bodies, and the consequent difference in their subsequent development. One point of difference is with regard to the giant explosion calderas, which appear to be the earliest volcanic structures on the Moon, and to be the larger the older they are. The visible counterparts of these structures on the Earth are much less common and much smaller, but it is possible that similar giant explosion calderas may have been formed more abundantly very early in the geological history of the Earth, and have been subsequently buried or destroyed, so that no trace of them can now be recognized. The folded mountain ranges, which are conspicuous features of the Earth's surface, do not seem to be reproduced on the surface of the Moon, possibly because the Moon's crust is much thinner and weaker than that of the Earth, offering less resistance to penetration upward by interior magma to form volcanoes on its surface, so that the relief from interior expansion is accomplished in this manner on the Moon instead of by structural adjustments in the crust itself.

Probably about a dozen volcanic eruptions can be observed to take place annually on the Earth's surface, and this number might be considerably increased if submarine eruptions also could be seen. Most terrestrial eruptions would be visible to an astronomer on the Moon, if furnished with instruments comparable to those possessed by Earthly observatories. Yet, in the hundred years or more during which the surface of the Moon has been under observation by sufficiently large sized telescopes on the Earth, not a single authenticated instance is known of a lunar volcanic eruption, as manifested by lava flows, volcanic explosions or the formation of new craters. The Moon, therefore, appears to be a finished world, while the Earth is still alive geologically and expanding in volume. This fact strongly supports the hypothesis that the center of the Earth is still occupied by a Nucleus of high-density, Sun-inherited atoms, whose disintegration is the cause of terrestrial vulcanism, while the similar nucleus, once existing in the Moon, has completed its disintegration. This significant conclusion suggests that the disintegration of such nuclei is dominantly peripheral, and hence that smaller nuclei complete their disintegration sooner than large nuclei, and that smaller heavenly bodies age faster than larger ones.

Through a high-powered telescope, the planets Mercury and Mars reveal alternating light-hued and dark-hued areas on their surfaces, similar to the aspect of the Moon to the naked eye, although, of course, the patterns are different. Dark-hued areas on the Earth, as seen by a lunar astronomer, could be due to four causes: (1) bodies of water; (2) cloud shadows; (3) recently burnt over areas; (4) recent basaltic lava flows. None of the first three can occur on the Moon, so that the last is the only possible alternative there, and the fact that no subsequent rock alteration or growth of vegetation can modify its pristine blackness, as on the Earth, accounts for the maintenance of its original aspect, as erupted, over vast periods of time.

Mercury probably closely resembles the Moon in its surface aspect, because it, too, has no atmosphere, and if it could be viewed through a sufficiently high-powered telescope, it would probably appear to be pock-marked by big calderas, with basaltic lava fields constituting the dark areas, the same as on the Moon.

Conditions on Mars are somewhat different, for, while it has no large and permanent bodies of water on its surface, and therefore can have no sedimentary formations of aqueous origin, it has a thin atmosphere, and can have accumulations of wind-borne sand and dust, as suggested by the dust-storms, which have been observed in its atmosphere. It seems probable, therefore, that the valleys and low areas of the planet are occupied by deposits of wind-transported sand and dust, through which only the tops of the higher mountains protrude; and this would account for the fact that there do not appear to be any mountains higher than 2,500 ft. on Mars, as compared with elevations of over 20,000 ft. on the Moon. The Martian landscape, therefore, would probably be somewhat similar, as to topography, to that of southwestern Arizona, where low mountains are separated by wide desert valleys of much greater area. The ruddy hue of Mars may be due in principal measure to this circumstance, since red shales and sandstones are abundant in many terrestrial formations of sub-aerial desert origin, particularly those of Triassic age,—the color being due to the oxidation of iron silicates in rock formations to reddish iron oxides. The landscape of Mars, therefore, is probably partially lunar in appearance, where it is igneous in origin and consists of volcanoes, calderas and lava flows, and partially terrestrial in appearance, where it is sedimentary in character, and consists of deserts of wind-blown detritus.

CHAPTER SEVEN

The History of the Earth

An acceptable theory of cosmogony, or the origin of the Universe, must agree with and harmonize the following:

1. The Second Law of Thermodynamics and the Law of the Degradation of Energy, according to which complex structures can change into simple ones, but the reverse process cannot take place,— at least permanently.

2. The fact that most of the celestial galaxies occur in the form of two-armed spirals, which could have been formed only through tidal action as the result of the attraction of much larger masses.

3. The fact that these galaxies seem to be dispersing at high speeds.

4. The wide range of sizes of the stars.

5. The wide range of temperatures of the stars.

6. The wide range of densities of the stars; and particularly the enormous densities possessed by some white dwarf stars.

7. The fact that, in the Solar System, all of the planets revolve around the Sun in the same direction, and nearly in the same plane; that they all rotate on their axes in the same direction; and that, with a few exceptions, all of the satellites behave similarly, with regard to their respective planets.

8. The fact that, in the Solar System, the planets and their satellites, although possessing only about 1/745th of the mass of the System, have about 98% of its angular momentum.

9. The fact that the Earth seems to be slowly expanding in volume.

10. The fact that the source of most of this expansion seems to be situated at the center of the Earth.

11. The fact that all of the phenomena of vulcanism and of orogeny can be explained, directly or indirectly, by terrestrial expansion.

12. The fact that the interior heat of the Earth seems to be much larger than can be accounted for simply by cooling from an original molten condition.

Of the two general hypotheses of cosmogony discussed in Chapter II,—the Evolutionary Hypothesis, which assumes that complex forms evolve from simple ones; and the Devolutionary Hypothesis, which assumes that complex forms degenerate into simple ones,— the latter seems to be much more closely in harmony with the conditions previously set forth, and accordingly the history of the Earth, as discussed in this chapter, will be considered under this hypothesis.

Although the Earth is the offspring of the Sun, it is of nearly contemporaneous age, having been formed when the Sun was parting from its own parent, which was a sub-fragment of the fragment of the "Primordial Mass," that eventually developed into the Milky Way galaxy. This sub-fragment will hereafter be referred to as the "parent fragment." On this occasion, as the Sun was separating from it, the attraction of the latter caused the formation of two tidal bulges on the Sun,—one pointing towards the "parent fragment" and the other in the opposite direction, according to the laws governing such tidal action. These two bulges lengthened into two tidal arms, similar to the tidal arms forming the spiral galaxies. The two solar tidal arms thus formed were not uniform and continuous, but consisted of a crowd of separate blobs of Sun-material, ranging in size from several thousand miles diameter down to very minute proportions, and composed of complex, high density Q-atoms, in the physical state of a viscous liquid or a plastic solid. One of the larger of these blobs, which was expelled from the Sun relatively late, as the Sun was rapidly receding from the "parent fragment," and the attraction of the latter was diminishing, eventually became the Earth and the Moon. The spiral curve along which this Earth-Moon blob started to depart from the Sun was eventually modified, by the attraction of the "parent fragment" and the mutual interference of the numerous bodies composing the Sun's spiral arms, into an elliptical orbit around the Sun. Soon after its separation from the Sun, the Earth-Moon blob divided by fission into two parts, —a large blob, which became the Earth, and a small blob, which became the Moon,—and the mutual repulsion between these two parts, due to the tidal action caused in each by the attraction of the other, forced them to separate further and further apart,—a process which is still continuing.

If the Earth-blob had retained, during its development, all of its original mass, it would probably have had eventually a specific gravity somewhere in the vicinity of 1.23, which is the average density of the four major planets, Jupiter, Saturn, Uranus and Neptune. But, because of its relatively small mass, the Earth lost, in the course of its development, about four fifths of its original mass, in the form of hydrogen, helium and other very light constituents, so that the heavier elements composing the remaining one fifth cause the Earth to have a specific gravity of about 5.52 at the present time. On the basis of the assumption that the Sun-material, of which the Earth was originally composed, consisted almost wholly of Q-atoms, with a specific gravity of about 60,000, the primordial Earth was a relatively small heavenly body, with a diameter of about 600 miles.

The history of the Earth, from the time of its secession from the Sun to the present time may be divided into two parts: (1) the luminous phase; and (2) the non-luminous phase. The luminous phase began when, after the separation of the Earth-blob from the Sun, the Q-atoms composing the former commenced to disintegrate on its surface, with the evolution of light and heat, forming a small luminous star, which may be called the "Earth-star." During this phase, the Earth-star progressed successively through the first six stages of normal star development, as described in Chapter II, p. 58: (1) a high density white dwarf star; (2) a normal blue star; (3) a normal white star; (4) a normal pale yellow star; (5) a normal yellow star; and (6) a normal red star. The Sun is so massive that its gravitational attraction is sufficient, in spite of its high temperature, to restrain the escape of practically all of the simpler and lighter atoms produced by the surface disintegration of its nucleus, so that these simpler atoms have collected to form a hot, thick atmosphere surrounding the nucleus of Q-atoms still surviving, and the Sun has probably lost very little of its mass since its secession from the "parent fragment." The Earth-star was so small, however, that its gravitational attraction was insufficient to completely restrain the velocities imparted by its high surface temperature to the disintegration products of the Q-atoms, so that the lighter elements, comprising all of the hydrogen and helium, together with some nitrogen, oxygen and other gases, escaped into surrounding space, and only the heavier and more complex of the disintegration products remained, to form a gaseous atmosphere enclosing the Nucleus of Q-atoms. The Nucleus, which was a mass of Q-atoms in the probable form of a viscous liquid or a plastic solid, maintained its physical state unaltered throughout the luminous phase, except for its progressive shrinkage in size due to peripheral disintegration; and while the heavier disintegration products accumulated around the Nucleus as an atmosphere, the loss of the lighter disintegration products caused the Earth to continuously lose mass, until at the end of this phase probably only about 30% of the original mass remained. Although the Earth originated at nearly the same time as the Sun, the much smaller size of the Earth's Nucleus caused its peripheral disintegration to advance much faster proportionately than that of the Sun, and consequently the Earth has progressed much more rapidly through the different stages of stellar development. Thus the Sun is still luminous and is only in the fifth stage,— that of being a yellow star,—while the Earth is far along in the seventh or dark star stage.

The Earth's non-luminous phase, which succeeded its luminous phase, will eventually embrace the last two stages in stellar development: the seventh or dark star stage and the eighth or dead star stage. The dark star stage, within which the Earth is at present situated, is separable into three divisions: (1) the Dominantly Gaseous Division; (2) the Dominantly Liquid Division; and (3) the Dominantly Solid Division. These latter distinctions refer only to the envelope of disintegration products surrounding the Nucleus, and the three divisions merge into one another. The non-luminous phase and the Dominantly Gaseous Division of the dark star stage commenced when the Earth's atmosphere, surrounding the Nucleus, although still completely gaseous, had dropped to a sufficiently low temperature in its outer portions,—probably somewhere about 1,000° C.,—that it did not shine with its own light. With further cooling, the heavier constituents of the Earth's gaseous atmosphere began to condense to liquid form, eventually creating a sphere of molten rock material (magma), surrounding the Nucleus, and itself enclosed by a thin atmosphere of uncondensed gases, probably consisting chiefly of water vapor, carbon dioxide and nitrogen. The great contrast between the thinness of the Earth's atmosphere and the tremendously thick atmospheres of the major planets, such as that of Jupiter (Figure 3 - 4), strongly suggests that the major planets retained all products of the peripheral disintegration of their central nuclei, while the Earth, during its luminous phase, lost practically all of its lighter gases, and its present atmosphere represents principally a later accumulation of volcanic gases, expelled from craters after the formation of the solid crust,—subject to modification through the agency of plant life, as later described.

With further decrease in the Earth's surface temperature, due to continued shrinkage of the Nucleus and accompanying decline in heat production, the outer part of the mass of molten rock material began to solidify, forming a crust, and this solidification progressed inward, as the heat production of the Nucleus continued to decline, thickening the solid crust at the expense of the still molten interior. In the early stages of solidification of the crust, a partial segregation of the constituents of the molten magma slowly took place,—quartz and feldspars tending to collect near the surface, while ferromagnesian minerals, with some native nickel-iron, tended to remain at lower levels.

During the Dominantly Liquid Division, the expansion of the Earth in volume, due to the disintegration of the Q-atoms, constituting the Nucleus, into simpler and bulkier atoms, had been readily effected within the molten material; but, with the formation of the solid Crust, restraint was imposed upon the Earth's interior expansion, and it was only by forcing the molten magma into and through the Crust, thus initiating vulcanism, that this situation was relieved. Since the degree and extent of vulcanism is a function of the expansion of the Earth in volume, which in turn is a function of the disintegration of the Nucleus, vulcanism, together with orogeny, the process of mountain building, which is a by-product of vulcanism, were far more widespread and active at the beginning of the Dominantly Solid Division than they have been since and are today; for, in conformity with the shrinkage of the Nucleus, these manifestations, since their vigorous inception, have been gradually decreasing, and will continue to do so until the Nucleus has entirely disappeared, whereupon all vulcanism and orogeny will permanently cease. The conclusion from theoretical grounds that vulcanism must have been much greater in the past than at the present time finds support in the fact that the proportion of igneous rocks, both intrusive and extrusive, to sedimentary rocks, as a world-wide condition, seems to be greater in older geological formations than in younger ones. Thus in the Archeozoic formations of the Canadian shield, igneous rocks greatly exceed sedimentary rocks in surface area, although extensive erosion has contributed somewhat to that effect by unroofing and exposing once hidden batholiths.

The Dominantly Solid Division contains three sub-divisions: (1) the Pre-aqueous Sub-division; (2) the Aqueous Sub-division;

and (3) the Geological Sub-division. The Pre-aqueous Sub-division commenced with the formation of a permanent solid Crust, at a surface temperature of probably somewhere between 800° C. and 1,000° C., and terminated when this temperature had dropped to that of the boiling point of water. During this sub-division, the temperature of the surface of the Earth was above that of the boiling point of water, and consequently bodies of water could not exist. The atmosphere, therefore, was heavily laden with water vapor, which was its dominant constituent at the commencement of this sub-division, and was continuously being increased by contributions of volcanic gases throughout it.

The Aqueous Sub-division commenced when the average surface temperature of the solid Crust had dropped below that of the boiling point of water. At the beginning of this sub-division, the water vapor, which previously had chiefly constituted the atmosphere, condensed to liquid form, creating surface bodies of water occupying large areas of the Crust, although they were doubtless less extensive than at present, and tended to form a series of large but separate lakes, rather than connected oceans, such as now cover more than 70% of the surface of the globe. Due to voluminous volcanic contributions of water vapor during this sub-division, the size of the surface bodies of water continuously increased, until they tended to connect and form oceans, as at the present time, although somewhat smaller.

The Geological Sub-division, which succeeded the Aqueous Sub-division without marked change, commenced when the oldest formations now visible on the Earth's surface were formed. They consisted entirely of intrusive and extrusive igneous rocks and sedimentary formations. No trace of the primitive crust, formed by congelation of the molten magma previously occupying the Earth's surface is visible among them, and it is probable that it, together with extensive masses of igneous rocks and of sedimentary formations of early origin, were deeply buried or destroyed by later vulcanism or erosion, before the formations now exposed were formed. The Geological Sub-division is divided into five eras, commencing with the Archeozoic and extending through the Proterozoic, Palaeozoic, Mesozoic and Cenozoic down to the present time; and these five eras are in turn subdivided into periods, epochs, etc., as fully described in geological literature.

In the early part of the Geological Sub-division, the oceans were probably smaller and less connected than at the present time. This conclusion is supported by the fact that the proportion of sedimentary formations of land or continental deposition to sedimentary formations of aqueous deposition seems, as a world-wide condition, to be much greater in the older geological formations than in the younger ones. This is conspicuously illustrated in the case of limestone and dolomite, which are almost wholly of marine origin. Thus, moving backward in time, limestone and dolomite, which are abundant in formations of the Palaeozoic era, become much less common in formations of the preceding Proterozoic era, and are scarcer yet in the still older formations of the Archeozoic era.

An important change in the composition of the Earth's atmosphere took place during the Aqueous and Geological Sub-divisions, if, as is considered almost certain, the composition of the volcanic gases, which are believed to have principally contributed to the formation of the Earth's atmosphere, was the same originally as it is now. At present the principal volcanic gases are water vapor, carbon dioxide and hydrogen, with chlorine, hydrogen sulphide, oxygen, nitrogen, argon and a few others as minor constituents. The water vapor condenses and precipitates upon the Earth's surface, while the hydrogen, chlorine, hydrogen sulphide and some of the oxygen and carbon dioxide form compounds with other elements. The residual constituents of the primitive atmosphere in the early part of the Aqueous Sub-division, therefore, were carbon dioxide, nitrogen, a little oxygen, and some minor constituents, principally argon. By way of contrast, the present atmosphere consists of about four fifths nitrogen and one fifth oxygen, after allowing for about 1% of minor constituents. Plant life appears to have been the agent that brought about the change; and plant life, in turn, was dependent on sunlight, which, after the thick clouds of water vapor, which had previously shrouded the face of the Earth in darkness, had condensed to water and precipitated upon the surface in the early part of the Aqueous Sub-division, was for the first time able to penetrate through the thin and transparent atmosphere that remained.

Oxygen, although the most common element in the Earth's crust, is so active chemically, that in volcanic gases it rarely occurs in elemental form, although it is abundant in combination with hydrogen to form water vapor (H_2O) and with carbon to form carbon dioxide (CO_2). However, the energy of sunlight, working upon chlorophyll, which constitutes the green coloring matter of plants, enables the chlorophyll, by the process called photosynthesis, to decompose carbon dioxide into carbon, which is incorporated into plant bodies, and into oxygen, which is released into the atmosphere; and it is probable that in this manner the present amount of free oxygen in the atmosphere has been gradually built up, at the expense of its large original content of carbon dioxide, which has now been reduced to about 3/100 of 1% and is maintained at that figure through the decay of plant life and the exhalations of animal life. All other planetary atmospheres of the Solar System, concerning which dependable information is available, seem to have little or no free oxygen, which is suggestive of the absence of all forms of life, except that on Venus, whose atmosphere appears to contain considerable carbon dioxide, plant life, but not animal life, might exist.

The total amount of carbon dioxide, once in the Earth's atmosphere, which has been reduced to supply its present oxygen content, can be roughly calculated from the amount of carbon present in elemental form in sedimentary rocks, in which, as dead plant material, it has been buried and thus preserved from oxidation and decay. Assuming the sedimentary rocks to constitute the equivalent of a shell half a mile thick surrounding the Earth; the elemental carbon—aside from that contained in coal beds—to be confined almost wholly to shales, which constitute about 80% of all sedimentary rocks; and the elemental carbon content of shales to average 0.80%; then the total elemental carbon content of sedimentary rocks would amount to about 7.24×10^{15} tons. The carbon present in the coal resources of the world, which latter were estimated in 1929 at 8.667×10^{12} tons, would amount to only about one thousandth of that amount, and hence not enough to materially change the result. Compared with this figure of 7.24×10^{15} tons of elemental carbon present in sedimentary rocks, the Earth's atmosphere contains 1.305×10^{15} tons of oxygen. Each unit of carbon, incorporated in plant structures through the decomposition of carbon dioxide, would release 2 2/3 units of oxygen to the atmosphere. It would appear, therefore, as if there were about sixteen times as much elemental carbon present in sedimentary formations as would be necessary to account for all of the oxygen in the Earth's atmosphere; but a very large amount of oxygen, possibly many times as much as that now present in the atmosphere, must have been absorbed in the oxidation of rocks of surface formations in the Earth's Crust, so that the equation may be very nearly in balance.

In order for plant and animal life to develop in an atmosphere notable for scarcity of oxygen and abundance of carbon dioxide, plant life on the Earth must have commenced first and have flourished long before animal life appeared; and it was only after plant life, through the process of photosynthesis, had replaced enough of the carbon dioxide with oxygen to provide the minimum requirements of animal life in this respect, that the latter developed. The presence of elemental carbon, which is generally supposed to represent buried plant life, in the oldest schists, representing metamorphosed shales, in the sediments of the early Archeozoic era, suggest that plant life existed before the oldest sediments now visible on the Earth's surface were deposited, and hence commenced in the Aqueous Sub-division.

Life made its appearance upon the surface of the Earth when conditions developed, that were favorable for its existence. These favorable conditions were: (1) the hospitable environment provided by a warm ocean, whose size prevented it from ever drying up; which maintained a fairly uniform temperature—above freezing but not too hot—over long periods of time; which supplied water—the chief constituent of plant and animal life; and which also provided certain mineral salts necessary for life; (2) an atmosphere, which supplied carbon dioxide and some oxygen, but did not contain any noxious gases in lethal amount; and (3) sunlight, which was the magician, that brought about the transformation of inorganic matter into living forms. Since sunlight and water are indispensable factors, life can exist only on planets whose atmospheres are so transparent as to permit sunlight to pass through, and which support large and permanent bodies of water on their surface; hence life must be only an accidental phase of planetary development, since only one or at most two planets of the Solar System can meet these conditions. Just how a living organism can evolve from inorganic matter is a secret of Nature not yet revealed, but it probably developed from colloidal material under the influence of the energy supplied by sunlight; doubtless such a transformation cannot take place without some exterior stimulus. The earliest forms of life probably consisted of minute, one-celled plant organisms of simple character, possibly belonging to the Algae (seaweed) family, which floated in warm oceanic water, and reproduced by subdivision. Animal life in its earliest stage was probably very similar, but it could not develop until a sufficient supply of atmospheric oxygen had become available, through the agency of plant life, to supply its minimum requirements. Although it is thought that plant life commenced in the Aqueous Sub-division, it is possible that animal life did not appear until in the Geological Sub-division. Well advanced forms of animal life left their fossil remains in sedimentary beds at the commencement of the Palaeozoic era, but the Archeozoic and Proterozoic eras, which preceded it, may have been sufficiently lengthy for the development of all antecedent forms. Life, both plant and animal, had its inception in the oceans, and thence, by adaptation, gradually spread over the land areas.

The Geological Sub-division still has some further time to run, but, as the Nucleus gradually grows smaller and less heat producing, vulcanism and orogeny will correspondingly slow down, until, when the Nucleus has entirely disappeared, they will completely terminate, and the solidification of the liquid Core of the Earth will have ended, with the body of the Earth solid throughout. With the disappearance of the Nucleus, the Geological Sub-division of the seventh or dark star stage of the Earth's development will end, and the Earth will enter upon the eighth and last, or dead star stage, when there will be no further interior activity or heat generation. Erosion will then continue to destroy the land areas, and as the latter will no longer be replenished by vulcanism and orogeny, the oceans will expand in area and will eventually cover all the face of the Earth. The Moon, the other satellites of the Solar System, the Asteroids, the planet Mercury and probably the planets Mars and Pluto, are already in that stage. As the Sun continues to cool, the terrestrial oceans will freeze, first on the surface, and then downwards until they are solid throughout, all life will previously have terminated, and the Earth, a dead planet, will circle about a dying and eventually dead Sun for eons of time.

During the preceding part of the Geological Sub-division, the average temperature of the Earth's surface seems to have been subject to fluctuations. There have been two forms of world climate: (1) a generally warm and genial climate, when the oceans were free of ice from pole to pole, and plants and animals, which are now confined to sub-tropical zones, flourished in much higher latitudes; and (2) a generally cool and rigorous climate, when the polar oceans were frozen over, and continental glaciers covered large land areas, extending down into the temperate zones, forming what are called glacial epochs. There have been four glacial epochs during the preceding portion of the Geological Sub-division, as recorded in geological formations: one during the early Proterozoic era; one during the late Proterozoic era; one during the Permian period of the Palaeozoic era; and one during the Pleistocene epoch of the Cenezoic era. The Earth is just emerging from the last one. Although there may have been a number of contributing causes of the formation of glacial epochs, there is no evidence that the Sun was in any way responsible, for the contributions of heat from that luminary seem to have been maintained at a uniform rate throughout the Geological Sub-division, so far as the evidence indicates. The principal cause of world-wide climatic fluctuations appears to have been the relative shape and distribution of land and water areas, which have not been constant, but have varied widely from time to time.

Open oceans extending uninterruptedly northerly and southerly so that the circulation of warm oceanic water from the tropics to the poles and return has been unimpeded seem to be necessary for a relatively mild world-wide climate. During these genial periods, the oceans also were more extensive than at present, probably covering about 80% of the Earth's surface, and the land areas consisted principally of large islands, similar to Australia at the present time, rather than connected continents like that of Europe-Asia-Africa. The free poleward movement of warm tropical oceanic currents promoted a warm and genial climate all over the globe, during which the differences between tropical and polar temperatures were much less extreme than at present.

During the glacial epochs, on the other hand, the land areas were increased in size and the ocean areas diminished,—the latter probably being reduced to about 70% of the Earth's surface. However, this relative increase in land area was not so important as its distribution. If these land areas did not block the northerly-southerly oceanic circulation, the effect would not be calamitous; but if such a circulation was impeded, no matter whether ample easterly-westerly circulation existed, the interference with the equalizing effect of oceanic circulation on zonal temperatures would bring about polar glaciation, which would extend down into adjacent portions of the temperate zones, and would be enhanced by the elevation of land areas and its cooling effect.

Thus, at the present time, as a survival of conditions that brought about the Pleistocene glacial epoch, there is no oceanic circulation across either polar zone. In the South Pacific Ocean, the center of the Antarctic Zone is occupied by the Antarctic continent, which covers about 5,470,000 square miles,—nearly 60% larger than Australia,—and has an average elevation of over 7,000 feet above sea-level, which is twice that of any other continent, although a considerable part of it must be due to the ice-cap which covers it. This completely ice-bound continent has such a refrigerating effect upon the average temperature of the Southern Hemisphere, that, despite the fact that the latter has a much greater water area than the Northern Hemisphere, the temperature of the Southern Hemisphere at 50° south latitude averages several degrees of temperature colder than at 50° north latitude. In the North Pacific, access to the north polar regions is also denied by the nearly touching continents of Asia and North America, as the small opening of Bering Strait does not permit the passage of any substantial amount of oceanic circulation. In the Atlantic Ocean, the Antarctic Continent similarly prevents southerly oceanic circulation across the center of the Antarctic Zone, and, while the ocean extends to the North Pole, Bering Strait prevents a complete circulation across the polar regions.

It seems probable that the recent Glacial epoch during the Quaternary Period, from which the Earth is just emerging, was brought about partly by the elevation of the Antarctic continent and partly by the elevation of the submarine ridge, which connects Greenland, Iceland, the British Isles and Scandinavia. At present the crest of the part of this latter ridge between Iceland and Scandinavia is sufficiently far below sea-level to permit a part of the warm, equatorially generated ocean current known as the "Gulf Stream" to cross above it and continue northerly into the Arctic Ocean, warming the shores of the British Isles, Iceland and Scandinavia in its passage, and reducing the average temperature of the Arctic Zone. It needed, during the Glacial epoch, only an elevation of this ridge from 1,000 to 2,000 ft. to form a landbridge, completely closing the water gap between Greenland, Iceland and Scandinavia, or at least sufficiently reducing and shallowing this gap so that an ocean current could not pass through. It seems fairly certain that this actually happened,—not once but four times, synchronizing with the four stages of the Glacial epoch,—and that each time the Gulf Stream was turned back, so that the present warming effect of that ocean current in the upper North Atlantic Ocean was lost, and the Arctic Ocean developed a much colder climate than now. The result each time was the growth of four large continental ice-caps in the Northern Hemisphere,—three in northern North America and one in northern Europe,—in addition to the Greenland ice-cap, which still survives. Continental glaciation, once initiated by changes in the configuration and distribution of the land and water areas, tends to prolong its life in other ways and by other means.

Thus, the imprisonment of large volumes of water, abstracted from the oceans, in the form of snow and ice, deposited on the land areas, lowers the ocean surfaces,—as much as 400 ft. below present levels during the height of the Glacial epoch,—and thus tends to increase the proportion of land area, with more or less consequent impairment of oceanic circulation. Also, the cooling effect of continental ice-caps increases the precipitation of snow, while the cloudiness over glacial areas retards melting.

The glacial epoch during the Permian period similarly seems to have been brought about by the blocking of northerly-southerly oceanic circulation between the tropics and south polar regions by the formation of an extensive easterly-westerly trending continent, known as Gondwanaland, which connected South America, southern Africa and Australia by land bridges, while a somewhat similar easterly-westerly trending continent in the Northern Hemisphere also interfered with access to the polar regions by oceanic currents. Consequently the tropical ocean, which lay between these two land masses, had little effect in equalizing temperatures over the Earth. The elevation of areas in the Southern Hemisphere at this time helped to make glaciation more intense in the latter hemisphere during this period, just as it was more widespread in the Northern Hemisphere during the Quaternary period. The distribution of land and water areas during the two glacial epochs in the Proterozoic Era cannot be readily determined, but there is every reason to suppose that glaciation at those times was brought about by similar causes.

The amount of water in the oceans greatly exceeds, in volume, the amount of land above sea-level, and if the surface of the Earth were to become a perfect spheroid, water would cover it to an average depth of between 8,500 and 9,000 ft. all over the Earth. The existence of continents and islands projecting above the surface of the oceans, therefore, is due to differential elevation of the Earth's Crust, where they lie. It is quite possible that, when the Crust solidified and took permanent shape, it was not a perfect spheroid, but contained some original elevations and depressions, due to lack of uniformity in the constitution of the Crust; but the present configuration of the land and water areas is wholly different, not only from any such primitive distribution, but also from many subsequent rearrangements. This circumstance, together with the periodical alternations of warm and genial with cool and rigorous climates is best explained by the interior expansion of the Earth's body, due to the disintegration of Q-atoms in the Nucleus and consequent formation of a larger volume of lighter atoms, which, as explained in Chapter VI, result in the development of pressure columns, producing bulges on the Earth's surface. These bulges may occur anywhere that the weight of the Earth's Mantle and Crust, pressing down upon the Core, happens at the time to be less than elsewhere. If they happen to occur under existing land areas, they tend to elevate the land areas still more, and coincidently to more or less reduce the oceanic areas and interfere with oceanic circulation; while if they happen to occur under existing oceanic areas, they tend to raise the surface of the oceans and cause the oceans to transgress on the land areas, thus increasing the oceanic areas and promoting oceanic circulation. The fact that the oceans cover about three quarters of the globe would tend to make the bulges, if somewhat uniformly distributed, occur about three times as abundantly beneath the oceanic areas as beneath the land areas, and thus the warm and genial climates, when the oceanic areas are expanded and northerly-southerly oceanic currents are promoted, should tend to last about three times as long as the cool and rigorous climates, when the oceanic areas are contracted and northerly-southerly oceanic circulation is interfered with. Some such time relationship seems to have actually occurred.

Unconformities supply the best evidence of bulges on the Earth's surface in the past. Unconformities record former periods of exposure of certain areas of the Earth's surface to erosion; and the most obvious instances occur where portions of the Earth's surface below sea-level, upon which sediments were being deposited, were elevated above sea-level, causing sedimentation to cease and to be replaced by erosion, which more or less extensively destroyed the formations thus exposed. Simultaneously, there would be a local break in the burial of aquatic forms of life in the form of fossils, which would measure the time interval covered by the unconformity. Subsequent depression of the area in question below sea-level again, with a resumption of sedimentation and the burial of fossils, would tend to emphasize the unconformity, particularly if there had been some tilting of that part of the Earth's Crust during the interval between the two periods of sedimentation, so that the bedding planes of one group of sediments would be inclined at an angle to those of the other. Unconformities are more or less local in their occurrence, although the major ones are sometimes of considerable areal extent; but none are world-wide. In the United

States and Europe, where geological mapping first began, the unconformities observed there, with their accompanying breaks in the fossil record, were utilized to establish the geological time divisions, which have been made of universal application; but unconformities elsewhere do not necessarily conform to this arrangement, as is well exemplified in South Africa, where major unconformities in some instances occur in the middle of geological time divisions, and not between them.

The fact that these crustal bulges may be of considerable size and may attain high elevations, and that they have in the past profoundly altered the relative sizes and configurations of the land and water areas of the Earth's surface can be illustrated by several current examples. Thus, in the western United States, marine sediments,—originally deposited below sea-level, of course,—now lie at elevations ranging from 5,000 feet to over 14,000 feet above sea-level over many thousand square miles; while the summit of Mt. McKinley in Alaska, 20,300 feet in height, the loftiest peak on the North American continent, is capped by marine shales, overlying the granite which constitutes the bulk of the mountain. In the Andes Mountains of South America, marine sediments outcrop at elevations of more than 10,000 ft. above sea-level over large tracts. In the Himalaya Range of central Asia, Tertiary marine sediments now lie in places at elevations of over 20,000 ft. above sea-level, and if these sediments once extended over the crest of Mt. Everest, but have since been eroded, as seems probable, they must have been elevated over 30,000 ft. since their deposition. Examples of this nature, showing where formations, originally deposited below sea-level, have since been lifted a mile or more, can be multiplied; and in each such case the elevation has been due to bulging of the Earth's Crust within the area in question, due to the effect of a pressure column in the Earth's Mantle below. It is logical to assume that depressions below sea-level of comparable extent have also taken place, and this conclusion has been verified by the discovery, by ocean sounding, of submerged land topographic forms, such as canyons and river valleys, which could hardly have been formed by sub-aqueous erosion, at considerable depths below sea-level. Where now are high mountains on the Earth's surface may once have been deep oceans, and vice versa.

At the present time, the sub-crustal bulging seems to be taking place principally beneath the land areas, as evidenced by the fact that almost all the active volcanoes, which are the surface manifestations of pressure columns below in the Earth's Mantle, are located on continents or on bordering islands, and few are known to occur well within oceanic areas. This relationship is appropriate for cool and rigorous climates, while during warm and genial periods the volcanoes should tend to concentrate in the oceanic areas and hence be submarine. Volcanoes can function as well under water as above it, except that the quicker chilling of lava streams under water would tend to make the lava accumulate closer around the craters of submarine volcanoes than around those of land volcanoes, so that the aprons of lava flows and other volcanic products surrounding submarine volcanoes would be less wide-spread and extensive. There would be no diminution of volcanic activity during the warm and genial periods, therefore, but, being largely sub-aqueous, it would be less apparent to the eye.

Climatically, the Earth now seems to be emerging from the Pleistocene Glacial epoch; but this epoch consists of several stages, separated by interglacial stages which were as warm as the present; and hence it is somewhat uncertain whether the Earth is merely in another such interglacial stage, with one or more glacial stages lying ahead, or whether the Pleistocene Glacial epoch is finally terminating, with a lengthy period of world-wide warm and genial climate in prospect for the future. Further alternations of world-wide warm and genial with cold and rigorous climates may be expected in the future, within the life of the Geological Sub-division, although the gradual shrinkage of the Nucleus and decline in Earth expansion may be expected to decrease the frequency of such alternations and to lessen climatic extremes.

Attempts at determining the age of the Earth have been made by four methods: (1) the amount of sodium in the ocean; (2) the amount of sedimentation; (3) radioactivity; and (4) astronomical methods. The results have been uncertain, discordant, and, with the exception of the last one, applicable only to a part of the history of the Earth.

Determination of the age of the ocean by means of the amount of sodium now and formerly dissolved in its waters,—sodium being the largest constituent of the mineral salts present, next to chlorine,—can be applicable, of course, only to that portion of the Earth's history, after the Crust became sufficiently cool to support bodies of water on its surface. This method of determination is based on the assumptions (1) that all of the sodium now and formerly present in the ocean,—some of it having been diverted into salt

beds and into sediments along with connate water,—has been contributed to it by rivers, to which surface and ground water, dis-
solving the sodium from soil and rock formations, have delivered it;
(2) that the amount of sodium in soluble form, annually discharged
by rivers into the ocean, has been uniform throughout the past,
and comparable to what is being delivered annually at the present
time; and (3) hence that the total amount of sodium now dissolved
in the waters of the ocean, plus that present in salt beds and sediments, divided by the present annual river contribution, will give
the time in years since the Crust of the Earth was sufficiently cool
to permit the existence of bodies of water on its surface. The total
amout of sodium in soluble form now and formerly in the ocean
has been estimated at 1.774×10^{16} tons, which, divided by the amount
of new sodium annually delivered by rivers to the ocean, estimated
at 6.360×10^{7} tons, would indicate, in round numbers, a period of
about 280,000,000 years.* The most uncertain factor in the calculation is the average amount of sodium delivered annually to the
ocean by rivers, and if the present rate is not a fair criterion of that
in the past, the result would be affected accordingly.

Attempt to determine the age of the Earth by the extent of
former sedimentation in the ocean can apply only to that period of
the Earth's history after the formation of a solid crust, at which
latter time sedimentation commenced. The method employed is to
measure the total thickness of all sediments, estimate the rate of
annual deposition, and divide to find the number of years required
to accomplish the result. The figures obtained by various investigators, using this method, have varied widely, ranging from about
100,000,000 years in the older estimates to over 1,000,000,000 years
in the later ones. The great obstacle in using this method of computation is the wide variation between the rates of sedimentation
in different parts of the ocean. Sedimentation is most abundant
closely offshore,—particularly in deltas and foredeeps,—and least
on the ocean bottom far from land, and since former off-shore sediments are more commonly exposed in rock formations than deep-sea
sediments, there has probably been a tendency to over-estimate the
average worldwide thickness of sediments. The most potent agents
of erosion, which provide the material for sediments, are usually
catastrophic in character, consisting of floods, high winds and earth-

*FOOTNOTE: *"Physics of the Earth, The Age of the Earth,"* p. 68, National
Research Council, Washington, D. C., 1931.

quakes, which, with glaciers, accomplish far more work of this nature in a short time than the gentler agents of erosion working over much longer periods. The fact that vulcanism and orogeny were much more active in the Aqueous Sub-division and the early part of the Geological Sub-division than they are now suggests that sedimentation must have taken place much more rapidly then than at present, and this conclusion is strengthened by the fact that land surfaces were probably not clothed by vegetation in the earlier geological times. Land vegetation seems to have first appeared at the beginning of the Devonian period of the Palaeozoic Era, while grasses, which are much more effective than any other forms of vegetation in protecting land surfaces from erosion, are first recognized in fossil form in the Lower Cretaceous formations. The greatly accelerated erosion to be observed at the present time on soils, from which grass or forest cover has been removed, provides an illustration of what probably happened in pre-Devonian times, when the land surfaces were entirely bare and unprovided with any protection aganist erosion. Considering these objections, it seems very doubtful whether the thickness of sediments can furnish a dependable method for computing the time that has elapsed since the beginning of the Aqueous Sub-division.

Attempt to determine the age of the Earth by means of radio-activity is based on the fact that uranium and thorium, as constituents of the Earth's Crust, are constantly disintegrating at a known rate, and that the end products of their disintegration are eight atoms of helium ($_2He^4$) and one atom of an isotope of lead ($_{82}Pb^{206}$) for each original atom of uranium, and six atoms of helium ($_2He^4$) and one atom of a different isotope of lead ($_{82}Pb^{208}$) for each original atom of thorium. If it were possible to arrest these end products, as fast as formed, and confine them to the immediate vicinity of the original atoms, it should then be possible theoretically to calculate, by means of the known rate of disintegration of the original atoms, and the relative weights of the original atoms and their end products present, the time that has elapsed since disintegration commenced, which presumably would be when the uranium and thorium atoms were formed. Therefore, by determining the amount of the lead isotope ($_{82}Pb^{206}$) or of helium closely associated with any uranium mineral, and the amount of the lead isotope ($_{82}Pb^{208}$) or of helium closely associated with any thorium mineral, it has been generally assumed that the age of the environment, in which the mineral occurred, or of the Earth itself, could be ascertained. The method is somewhat like that of determining how long a coal fire has been burning, from the known rate of combustion of the coal, and the relative amounts of ashes and unburnt coal present. Unfortunately, other considerations affect the validity of this conclusion, and of the calculations based thereon.

In the first place, probably all samples of uranium and thorium minerals, which have been tested in this manner, have been taken from ore deposits, as it is only in such localities that such minerals occur in sufficient concentration to permit accurate analysis. Uranium and thorium minerals in ore deposits are almost invariably accompanied by other minerals, among which the lead mineral galena (PbS) or oxidized lead minerals derived therefrom are frequent.

The lead in galena and all other common lead minerals is a mixture of four isotopes of lead in the following approximate proportions:

$$\begin{array}{lc}
Pb^{204} & 1.5\% \\
Pb^{206} & 23.6\% \\
Pb^{207} & 22.6\% \\
Pb^{208} & 52.3\% \\
\hline
\text{Average:} \quad Pb^{207.21} & 100.0\%
\end{array}$$

Any galena or other common lead mineral associated with an uranium mineral, therefore, will also contain Pb^{206}, and any galena or other common lead mineral associated with a thorium mineral will also contain Pb^{208}, so that the amount of lead present, or even of Pb^{206} or Pb^{208} present, cannot be assumed to be necessarily a derivative of uranium or of thorium, and hence cannot be used with confidence as an index of their age. It will be necessary to determine what portion of any Pb^{206} or Pb^{208} present is to be attributed to accompanying lead minerals, before the amount of such lead isotopes presumed to be derivatives of uranium or thorium can be ascertained. The uranium-helium ratio and the thorium-helium ratio are even less dependable, because helium can be introduced into ore deposits by mineralizing agencies in variable amount, entirely independent of uranium and thorium, while helium originally present, being a gas, may be depleted in simliar fashion.

The method is further limited by the fact that in a gaseous or liquid environment, any end products formed would not accompany the uranium and thorium minerals, but would tend to separate from them. It is only in a solid medium that such end products would tend to remain in juxtaposition to the uranium and thorium minerals, from which they were derived. Hence radioactivity would not record the period that uranium and thorium were in a gaseous or liquid state, but only the length of time they were immobilized in solid formations. Consequently the maximum age that uranium and thorium can register is not the entire age of the Earth, but only the period since the formation of a solid Crust, and not even that if these elements have since been transported from their original environment by mineralizing agencies. Minerals are conveyed in a liquid or gaseous medium to the places, where they are found in ore deposits, and in the course of such transfer uranium and thorium would necessarily be separated from any lead and helium that they might formerly have produced; consequently, uranium and thorium present in ore deposits can record only the time, since such ore deposits were formed, which will have no necessary relationship to the age of the host rocks. Ore deposits are always younger than the rock formations, in which they occur, and often far younger,— many ore deposits, which occupy Proterozoic formations, being themselves of Tertiary age. The function of uranium and thorium as time indicators, therefore, must be restricted to the time of their emplacement in the solid Crust of the Earth, where they now occur. Analyses which involve determination of the amounts of different isotopes of lead present, are of great delicacy, and are subject to a considerable factor of error, so that the results must be received with considerable skepticism, unless all proper precautions are known to have been observed, and unless the results harmonize with other evidence. Conclusions based on the assumption that all the lead accompanying the uranium and thorium minerals is necessarily a derivative of them, as was the case with nearly all of the early determinations, must be considered to be of very doubtful validity, while conclusions based on the assumption that all lead present in the form of the isotopes Pb^{206} and Pb^{208}, accompaning uranium and thorium minerals, is necessarily a derivative of them, are similarly open to question. Subject to the conditions and limitations previously stated, results obtained by this method should be of value, if properly interpreted, but they do not deserve the unquestioning acceptance they seem to have received in the past.

It is only by means of astronomical data that the total age of the Earth, from the time of its parting from its parent, the Sun, down to the present moment, can be estimated with any degree of probability. As discussed in Chapter II, it has been estimated, from the speed of the flight of the galaxies, that the age of the Universe, from the time of the beginning of the break-up of the Primordial Mass, was probably somewhere between 2,000,000,000 and 4,000,000,000 years, with the chances favoring the larger number. Just when during this period, the birth of the Sun and the nearly contemporaneous birth of the Earth took place is uncertain, but it seems not unlikely that it may have been about halfway, which would place the age of the Earth at somewhere between 1,000,000,000 and 2,000,000,000 years,—more probably near the latter. A tentative figure of 1,600,000,000 years has been arrived at by the calculation on Page 85, although this is based on assumptions, which cannot be verified. For purposes of discussion, and in default of any more certain figure, however, 2,000,000,000 years has been arbitrarily adopted as what the total age of the Earth will be upon the completion of the present Geological Sub-division, and the passage of the Earth into its eighth and final stage,—that of a dead star.

An estimate of the changes in the mass of the Earth and of the extent of the transfer of material from the disintegrating Nucleus

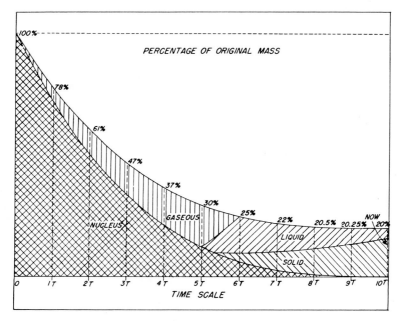

FIGURE 7 - 1

Illustrating graphically the changes in the mass of the Earth, and the extent of the transfer of material from the disintegrating Nucleus to its end products in the gaseous, liquid and solid physical states, at different stages in the Earth's development.

into its simpler end products in the gaseous, liquid and solid states, at different stages during the Earth's development, is shown graphically in Figure 7 - 1, which has been arbitrarily divided into ten time units of 200,000,000 years each. About 80% by weight of the end products of the disintegration of the Q-atoms composing the Earth's Nucleus are assumed to be equal proportions of hydrogen and helium, which escaped completely from the Earth's gravitational control, during its development, and dispersed into space. The remaining 20% by weight are assumed to consist of the heavier elements, which were retained within the Earth's gravitational control, and, as the Earth cooled, formed its present body. From the average composition of meteoric material, as estimated on Page 112, which the average composition of the body of the Earth—except for undisintegrated and partially disintegrated Nucleus—is believed to resemble, this average composition of the Earth's body is assumed to be about as follows:

Oxygen	40.0 %
Silicon	21.25%
Iron	19.25%
Magnesium	12.0 %
Calcium	3.25%
Aluminum	2.25%
Miscellaneous	2.00%
	100.00%

On such a basis, the total end products of the disintegration of the Q-atoms, originally composing the Earth, would be about as follows:

Hydrogen	40.0 %
Helium	40.0 %
Oxygen	8.0 %
Silicon	4.25%
Iron	3.85%
Magnesium	2.40%
Calcium	.65%
Aluminum	.45%
Miscellaneous	.4 %
	100.00%

The lengths of the different stages of the Earth's development, previously discussed on pages 207-211, have been estimated in round numbers on the accompanying time scale (Table XIII), but these estimates are subject to so large a factor of error, that they can be considered only as tentative and provisional, valuable chiefly for illustrative purposes. The place of the present, marked NOW on the graph shown in Figure 7 - 1, has been suggested by the fact that the Earth's Nucleus appears to have shrunk to a very small size, indicating that the end of the Geological Sub-division is relatively not far distant. The length of the Geological Sub-division, representing all rock formations now visible on the Earth's surface, is shown as being far shorter than any of the various estimates appearing in geological text-books; but such estimates have been based on the wholly unsupported assumption that geological activities in the past have been on the same scale as at the present time, whereas it has been shown on previous pages that there is good reason to believe that volcanic and orogenic activities at the commencement of the Geological Sub-division were many times greater than at present, and that, until the clothing of land surfaces by a protective cover of vegetation, which commenced about the middle of the Palaeozoic era but was not completed until much later, erosion and sedimentation were also many times greater than at present. On this latter basis, the allowance for the Geological Sub-division on the time scale would be adequate. Furthermore, the preceding Aqueous Sub-division represents, in a way, an extension of the Geological Sub-division backward in time, differing from the latter only through the fact that none of the rock formations emplaced during the Aqueous Sub-division are now visible on the Earth's surface.

TABLE XIII

TIME SCALE

	Years
Luminous Phase	
Progress of the Earth, as a luminous star, successively through the first six stellar stages: (1) a high density dwarf white star; (2) a normal blue star; (3) a normal white star; (4) a normal pale yellow star; (5) a normal yellow star; and (6) a normal red star.	1,000,000,000
Non-luminous phase	
Progress of the Earth through stage (7) as a normal dark star.	
1. The Dominantly Gaseous Division:	100,000,000
2. The Dominantly Liquid Division:	400,000,000
3. The Dominantly Solid Division:	
(a) Pre-aqueous Sub-division:	200,000,000
(b) Aqueous Sub-division:	200,000,000
(c) Geological Sub-division:	
(1) From its beginning to the present time:	
(a) Archeozoic era	
(b) Proterozoic era	
(c) Palaeozoic era	
(d) Mesozoic era	
(e) Cenozoic era	
	95,000,000
(2) From the present time to its end:	5,000,000
	1,000,000,000
Total	2,000,000,000

In the history of the Earth, human life is a geological pheno-menon of only trivial importance, although of surpassing interest to the human race itself. The elevation of the human animal above all its fellow animals has been chiefly accidental, being traceable initially to a single point of difference, although other differences have since developed. In all other respects the human animal was originally not outstanding, for it was weaker in physical strength and in bodily armament than many of its animal contemporaries, in an encounter with which it could save itself only by flight to some haven of refuge, such as trees, cliffs or caves. Even in brain capacity it did not excel some others at the time, probably somewhere between 100,000 and 1,000,000 years ago, when the lines of descent of the human animal and the anthropoid apes diverged from a common ancestor. It was to be expected that the dominant animal of the Earth would be a mammal rather than a reptile, because the warmer blood of the mammal, aided by a fur coat, a thick hide, and a subcutaneous layer of fat, would enable it to adjust itself to temperatures much lower than those, which would be fatal to a reptile. Also the young of the mammal is much better guarded and protected in infancy than that of the reptile. It was also to be expected that the dominant animal would be an inhabitant of the land rather than of the sea, because the land permits a much wider variety of activities than does the sea, enables the construction of permanent habitations, and offers more opportunities for survival amid enemies.

With few exceptions, the four limbs of all mammals, together with those of birds, are used principally for locomotion, and are capable of other uses only to a limited extent. The most prominent exception has been the human animal, which uses only the two hind limbs for locomotion, and so has the two fore limbs free for other uses. The fore limbs of the human animal are exceptional in that they terminate in hands, which, mounted at the ends of arms of considerable length and flexibility, are tools of marvellous adaptability and can be used for a wide variety of purposes. The apes and monkeys also possess similar hands, but they are handicapped by the fact that their feet are far less serviceable than human feet, being limited to use only in arboreal life, which greatly restricts their activities. The human animal, therefore, is the only one possessing hind limbs equipped with feet, well adapted for locomotion in a wide variety of environments, and fore limbs terminating in hands, which are entirely free for other uses and are capable of many such uses; and it was to this circumstance originally that the human animal, although in other respects not differing materially from its fellow animals, owed the beginning of the pre-eminence it has since attained. The chief physical differences from other animals, that the human animal has since acquired, are increases in brain capacity and quality, which have given it enlarged and improved mental powers, and improvements in its vocal organs, which enable it to produce a great variety of sounds and thus aids the capacity for communication with others.

Not only can the human hands be used directly for many purposes, but they are capable of making a great variety of tools, thus equipping the human animal to an extent that much more than offsets its inferiority to certain other animals in physical strength. With these hands it was possible, at first, to supplement the natural armament of the human animal with clubs and stones for missile and striking weapons; then gradually more effective weapons were devised, together with tools and implements for other purposes. The preparation of skins for clothing, the construction of habitations, the taming of fire, the domestication of certain animals, the domestication of certain plants, and other advances in primitive civilization followed, and with each advance the capacity of the human brain increased and its quality improved. The most important developments in the history of the human race have been those of a spoken language and of writing. The development of a spoken language was not unique, since many animals and birds are able to converse to a limited extent, by sounds denoting the primitive ideas of love, fear, hatred, pain, pleasure, defiance, danger, etc.; but the great increase in the number of meanings which the human animal is able to convey by sounds has enabled it to profit by the experience of its fellows instead of being dependent solely upon its own experience. The invention of writing, whereby objects and ideas were first indicated by pictures and then by symbols, following which sounds were denoted by symbols, has been an equally important step in human progress, because it has enabled the experience of multitudes of people, living and dead, to be assembled in books and records, which constitute a vast storehouse of knowledge, available to all.

Although in the relatively short past life of the human race, it has made remarkable progress in the accumulation and utilization of knowledge, its social organization is still deficient in many important features, and substantial improvement in this respect must be achieved before the race can attain social stability. Among the important social problems awaiting attention,—all more or less interconnected, so that the solution of any one of them will help all the others,—are the prevention of dictatorships, the prevention of war (caused by dictators 90% of the time), the prevention of crime, the prevention of over-population, the elimination of poverty, and the establishment of equality of opportunity,—all of which must be successfully solved without repressing or impairing individual initiative, actuated by self-interest, which is the main-spring of human activity, and the principal secret of its progress in the past. Considering the present rate of advancement, almost by geometrical progression, it seems probable that all of these objectives will be attained within the next thousand years or less. Civilization,—not yet 20,000 years old,—is still only in its early youth, and future generations will look back upon the present with the same criticism of its sins of omission and commission, as that with which we regard the shortcomings of mediaeval society.

The future progress of the human race will probably be limited only by those impassable barriers, which exist within the Universe. Despite the approaching (from a geological standpoint) running down of the interior mechanism of the Earth, it should continue to be habitable for millions of years to come; for the habitability of the Earth is determined principally by the amount of heat and light furnished by the Sun, which should continue for some millions of years in the future at only a very slowly diminishing rate. The principal effect of the completion of the disintegration of the Earth's Nucleus, five million years or so hence, will only be that thereafter there will be nothing to offset the effects of erosion, which will gradually reduce the land surfaces, so that eventually all will be submerged beneath the ocean; but that will probably be many millions of years distant.

Space travel for the purpose of exploring for celestial bodies, other than the Earth, suitable for human occupancy, will probably be fruitless, even if mechanically possible, and if not prevented by the great danger of collision with high velocity meteorites, which throng interstellar space, because no other planet and no satellite of the Solar System seems to be habitable at the present time, although Venus may become so millions of years hence. Among the billions of other stars like the sun, there must be billions of planetary systems, since the formation of such a tributary system seems to be a normal feature in the development of a star. And in these billions of planetary systems, there must be many millions of planets as suitable for the development of life as is the Earth, and many of them may be inhabited by beings equal or superior in intelligence to the human race. But if the speed of light is the fastest possible speed, then only the nearer stars in the Milky Way galaxy,—such as the star Proxima Centauri, which is 4.3 light years distant,—will ever be accessible, since the vast majority of the stars are thousands and millions of light-years distant, and are still rapidly receding. It seems most probable that the human race must be content with the Earth,—the beautiful planet,—as an abiding place, for which it will serve for millions of years to come, sufficient for the human race to thoroughly explore and exploit all its own potentialities.

Acknowledgments

Acknowledgment is herewith made of helpful information supplied by the following books and periodicals.

"*Astronomy,*" by H. N. Russell, R. S. Dugan and J. Q. Stewart.
Copyright, 1945, Ginn & Company, New York, N. Y.

"*Classical and Modern Physics,*" by Harvey E. White.
Copyright, 1940, D. Van Nostrand Company, Inc., New York, N. Y.

"*Climate Through The Ages,*" by C. E. P. Brooks.
1926, R. V. Coleman, New York, N. Y.

"*Earthquakes,*" by Nicholas Hunter Heck.
Copyright, 1936, Princeton University Press, Princeton, N. J.

"*Encyclopedia Brittanica.*"
1949, University of Chicago, Chicago, Illinois.

"*Igneous Rocks and the Depths of the Earth,*" by R. A. Daly.
Copyright, 1933, McGraw-Hill Book Company, Inc., New York, N. Y.

"*Internal Constitution of the Earth,*" edited by Beno Gutenberg.
Copyright, 1939, McGraw-Hill Book Company, Inc., New York, N. Y.

"*Internal Constitution of the Earth,*" edited by Beno Gutenberg.
Copyright, 1951, Dover Publications, Inc., New York, N. Y.

"*Introduction to Modern Physics,*" by F. K. Richtmyer and E. H. Kennard.
Copyright, 1947, McGraw-Hill Book Company, Inc., New York, N. Y.

"*Life on Other Worlds,*" by H. Spencer Jones.
Copyright, 1940, The MacMillan Company, New York, N. Y.

"*Our Mobile Earth,*" by R. A. Daly.
Copyright, 1926, Charles Scribner's Sons, New York, N. Y.

"*Outlines of Historical Geology,*" by Charles Schuchert.
Copyright, 1931, John Wiley & Sons, Inc., New York, N. Y.

"*The Age of the Earth*," by Adolph Knopf and others.
1931, National Academy of Sciences, Washington, D. C.

"*The Composition of the Earth's Crust*," by F. W. Clarke and H. S. Washington.
1924, U. S. Geological Survey, Professional Paper No. 127, Washington, D. C.

"*The Data of Geochemistry*," by F. W. Clarke.
1924, U. S. Geological Survey, Bulletin No. 770, Washington, D. C.

"*The Earth and the Stars*," by C. G. Abbot.
Copyright, 1946, D. Van Nostrand Company, Inc., New York, N. Y.

"*The Nature of the Physical World*," by A. S. Eddington.
Copyright, 1928, The MacMillan Company, New York, N. Y.

"*The Ore Magmas*," Vols. I & II, by J. E. Spurr.
Copyright, 1923, McGraw-Hill Book Company, Inc., New York, N. Y.

"*The Universe Around Us*," by Sir James Jeans.
Copyright, 1931, The MacMillan Company, New York, N. Y.

"*Volcanoes As Landscape Forms*," by C. A. Cotton.
1944, Whitcombe & Tombs, Inc., Auckland, New Zealand.

Various articles by various authors, too numerous to be listed, in the periodicals: "*Astrophysical Journal*," "*American Journal of Science*," "*Journal of Geology*," "*Economic Geology*," "*Physical Review*" and "*Reviews of Modern Physics*."

Special thanks are due three members of the faculty of the University of Wisconsin, Madison, Wisconsin: Prof. W. W. Beeman, of the Department of Physics; Prof. A. E. Whitford, of the Department of Astronomy; and Prof. L. R. Ingersoll, of the Department of Physics; who, while not subscribing to the unconventional ideas set forth herein, have kindly supplied much helpful information and advice. Subject to the same reservation, Prof. A. E. Whitford has also critically read Chapter II, while Prof. W. W. Beeman has critically read the entire manuscript.

Index